RUSSIAN FOLK TALES

RUSSIAN

FOLK TALES

Translated by Natalie Duddington

Illustrated by Dick Hart

Funk & Wagnalls, New York

© Copyright 1967 by Natalie Duddington
First published by Rupert Hart-Davis, London.

First published in the United States, 1969, by
Funk & Wagnalls, *A Division of* Reader's Digest Books, Inc.
Library of Congress Catalogue Card Number: 69–12152
Printed in the United States of America
1

Contents

6   *Contents*

Introduction

The folk tales in this volume have been selected from the famous collection made about a hundred years ago by Afanasyev. He was the first to make a systematic record of Russian folk stories which had never appeared in book form before. A few of them could be found among the works of various Russian authors: Pushkin put into verse several folk stories told him by his nurse, Arina Rodionovna; S. T. Aksakov records a peasant version of "Beauty and the Beast" in *A Russian Schoolboy*; Zhukovsky gives, in a high-flown style and greatly romanticized form, an old Russian folk story "The Three Girdles"; Gogol introduces several Ukrainian folk tales in *Evenings on a Farm Near Dikanka*. But it was not till the middle of the nineteenth century that Russian folklore became an object of study. Afanasyev, and others after him, wrote down folk stories as told by local country people, mostly women, who were known to be particularly good at doing this. Much material has been gathered and published, but probably much still remains as oral tradition. In one of Ertel's novels, written in 1888, there is a delightful description of an evening in a peasant cottage where numbers of children gather to hear the blind old grandmother telling fairy tales. As late as 1930, a friend of mine heard a *raconteuse* in the province of Archangel telling a "droll" story not included in any printed collection.

There is no knowing whether such storytellers still exist in Russia, or whether Soviet children care for these tales at all. Recent Russian publications of folk tales include humorous stories making fun of the clergy and the upper classes, animal stories, and a few well-known tales, such as "The Firebird," but I have not seen any reprints of the collection from which the stories in the present volume have been taken.

The nature of the country and its historical past have no doubt much bearing upon its folklore; it seems no mere coincidence that many of the gruesome stories collected by some of Afanasyev's successors belong to the gloomy regions of the North. As to the historical past of Russia, it is plainly reflected in the conviction of the people that it is useless to struggle against the powers that be, and that only divine intervention in one form or another can save the innocent. Many of the stories in the present volume bear this out. The way in which the characters in the tales react to circumstances throws a great deal of light on the Russian attitude to life; and since, in the last resort, a people's history is largely determined by their national character, study of a country's folklore, which reflects it, helps us to understand the people's historical destinies. The Russians, as they appear in the folk tales, have wonderful staying power, great fortitude in facing suffering and death, devotion to duty—but it never occurs to them to resist, to disobey orders, or even to run away when the whole world is open to them. The old man in "Daughter and Stepdaughter" sadly exposes his beloved daughter to mortal danger at the request of his nagging wife, and the same thing happens in "Master Frost"; the good peasant in "Straight and Crooked" does not even attempt to seek justice against his cheating employer; Ivan Tsarevitch in "Marya Morévna" is resigned to being killed by the old wizard. The women are always far more resourceful and capable of dealing with the situation.

Many interesting comparisons could be drawn between the different nations' psychology as revealed in their folklore, but that is a subject that needs a whole volume to itself.

Another subject, equally fascinating, and one on which a great deal of research has been done, is that of the origin of the different stories. Have they once had the same home, or do the resemblances between them spring from the essential identity of the human nature and the timeless pattern of cosmic life? It would be presumptuous to pass judgment on the matter without having studied the subject thoroughly; in compiling the present volume I have simply tried to select stories which are, to the best of my knowledge, with the exception of a few, peculiar to Russian folklore. I have purposely omitted some well-known tales that have already appeared in various English translations.

NATALIE DUDDINGTON

Daughter
and Stepdaughter

There lived once an old man whose wife died when their only daughter was still a child. After a time he married again, taking a widow who also had a daughter. The little girls grew up together, but they were very different from each other. The old man's pretty daughter, Masha, was kind, modest, and hard-working, and the old woman's daughter was spiteful, lazy, and ugly. The stepmother hated poor Masha and made her life a misery, especially when she found that the best young men in the village sought Masha in marriage while they would not even look at her own daughter. At last she could bear the girl's presence no longer and decided to get rid of her altogether.

"Take your daughter to the forest hut," she said to her husband one day. "She will do more spinning there than at home."

The old man protested that the hut was not a safe place; there were wild beasts in the forest and they could easily break through the door. But as this was precisely what his wife wanted to happen, she took no notice of his words, and kept on nagging at him till he gave way. He harnessed the horse, told Masha to get into the cart, and drove her to the forest hut. He gave her flint and steel to light a fire, a bag of millet to make porridge, and went home.

All day long the girl sat spinning; toward evening she heated the stove and cooked her supper. Suddenly a little mouse peeped out of its hole and begged: "Please, kind maiden, give me a spoonful of your porridge."

"Have as much as you like, dear little mouse! I am very glad of your company."

The mouse ate its fill and went away.

At midnight a big bear broke into the hut. He brought with him a small silver bell and said to Masha: "There, my girl, take this bell, put out the light, and let's play blind man's buff."

Masha was terrified, but the mouse climbed onto her shoulder and whispered in her ear: "Don't be afraid! Say 'yes,' put out the light, and climb on top of the stove, and I'll run about with the bell instead of you."

Masha obeyed. The bear ran after the mouse, but for the life of him could not catch it. The bell would ring now in one corner of the room, now in another, and he did not know which way to turn. He growled with fury and at last grew so hot and exhausted that he had to give up.

"Well, my girl," he said, "you are very good at the game! I'll send you a fine present tomorrow as a reward."

When the bear had gone, Masha thanked the mouse and slept in peace. In the morning she looked out of the window and saw that there was a cartload of silver in the yard and a drove of horses —the bear's present to her.

Meanwhile her wicked stepmother sent the old man to see how much spinning Masha had done. She was sure that Masha had been eaten by wild beasts and that nothing but bones was left of her. To celebrate the occasion she decided to make pancakes for dinner. While she was busy at the stove she heard the dog barking: "Bow-wow! The old man is bringing his daughter, and a drove of horses and a cartload of silver!"

"Hush, you vile cur! It's the girl's bones rattling in the cart! Here, have a pancake and be quiet!"

The dog ate the pancake and began again: "Bow-wow! The old man is bringing his daughter, and a drove of horses, and a cartload of silver."

She flung another pancake to the dog to keep it quiet, but as soon as it had eaten the pancake, it began the same story. She seized the poker to hit the dog, but at that moment she saw through the window that the old man had come into the yard with a drove of horses and a cartload of silver—and Masha, gay and rosy, was sitting next to him in the cart!

The old woman was beside herself with anger and envy. Without waiting for her husband and stepdaughter to come into the house, she ran out into the yard shouting: "When my daughter goes to the forest hut, she'll bring home two droves of horses, and two cartloads of silver!"

Next day the old man took her daughter to the forest hut. He gave her flint and steel and a bag of millet and left her there.

The lazy girl did not do any spinning, but just sat by the window idling away the time. In the evening she made for herself a huge potful of porridge and sat down to supper. A little mouse peeped out of its hole and asked: "Please give me a spoonful of your porridge, kind maiden."

"What next! Be off with you, you nasty creature! There's barely enough for myself," answered the girl, and she threw the spoon at the mouse. The mouse was frightened and hid itself in its hole. The girl ate up all the porridge, put out the light, and lay down to sleep.

At midnight the bear broke into the hut. He heard the girl snoring and walked straight up to her. "Take this bell," he said, "and let's play blind man's buff. You must run and I'll try and catch you."

The girl took the bell and ran, but her hand was shaking and the bell rang continuously—and the mouse peeping out of its hole

said over and over again: "The bad girl will come to a bad end." The bear soon caught her and ate her up.

In the morning the old woman sent her husband to the forest: "Go and fetch my daughter! She'll bring two droves of horses and two cartloads of silver!"

Presently she began frying pancakes for her daughter's dinner. The little dog outside the window barked: "Bow-wow! The old woman's daughter will never come back; the old man is alone in the cart, and her bones are rattling in a sack."

"That's a wicked lie, you vile cur! My daughter is coming home with droves of horses and cartloads of silver. There, have a pancake and say: 'The old woman's daughter good luck betide, but her stepsister shall be no man's bride.' "

The dog ate up the pancake and began again: "Bow-wow! Of the old woman's daughter nothing but bones remain, but the old man's daughter a happy home shall gain."

The old woman did all she could to silence the dog—threw pancakes to it, beat it, but to no purpose, for suddenly she looked up and saw that the old man had driven up to the gate and there was no one beside him in the cart. She ran out to meet him, and he gave her a sack with her daughter's bones. She set up a terrible wail and was so angry with him that she died that very day of grief and malice.

The old man found a good husband for Masha and they all lived happily together in peace and plenty.

The Fox
and the Hare

A fox* and a hare built themselves each a house in the forest; the fox's was made of ice, and the hare's of bark. The fox was very proud of her house, for it sparkled in the sun and was beautifully light within, and scorned the hare's dark little hovel. However, they lived like good neighbors all through the winter.

The spring came, the air grew warmer every day, and in the sunshine it was positively hot. One day Mrs. Fox came home from hunting and found that her ice house had melted away—nothing was left of it. Without losing a moment, she got into the hare's house and settled there. When the hare came home, she drove him away saying it was her house and not his.

The poor hare sat down in the path and wept bitterly. A wolf came along and asked what ailed him. The hare told him what had happened. The wolf was kindhearted and he felt sorry for the hare; besides, he was at loggerheads with the fox. "I'll drive that vixen out of your house," he said, and marched off.

* Fox (Lisá or Lisítsa) is always feminine in Russian folklore, whereas in English folklore it is always masculine. It often bears the name of Lizaveta Ivanovna or Lisá Patrikeyevna (daughter of Patrick).

But as soon as Mrs. Fox saw the wolf approaching, she thrust her head out of the door and called menacingly: "If I jump out and fight you, there will be little left of your fur!"

The wolf was alarmed and retreated. "It's no good, brother," he said to the hare as he passed him, and the poor hare wept more piteously than before.

A bear walked past and asked why he was crying. The hare told him his story, and the bear too was indignant with the fox. "I'll drive the wicked creature away," he growled, and walked to the hare's house.

But the bear's courage failed him when Mrs. Fox thrust her head out of the door and cried viciously: "If I jump out and fight you, there will be nothing left of your fur!" He turned back and had nothing to say to the hare as he passed him.

The hare had now lost all hope of retrieving his house, and his tears fell fast. A cock happened to go by and asked what was the matter. When he heard the hare's story, he too volunteered to drive away the fox. But the hare shook his head and said: "No, brother cock, it's no use your attempting it! The wolf tried and failed, the bear tried and failed, so how can you hope to succeed?"

"Wait and see," said the cock, and he strutted valiantly to the hare's house, singing at the top of his voice: "Cockle-doodle-do! My sword is sharp and true, I'll cut the fox in two!"

When Mrs. Fox heard this, she rushed out of the door in a panic and was never seen in the neighborhood again.

The hare was delighted, and invited the cock to come and live with him.

Lynx of the Forest

There once was an old man who had a beautiful daughter. They lived in peace and quiet until he married again. His second wife turned out to be a wicked witch; she took a dislike to her step-daughter and treated her badly. She kept saying to her husband: "Drive the girl out of the house—I can't bear the sight of her."

The old man thought things over and married his daughter to a good man who was well-off and lived quite near. The young couple were very happy together and soon a son was born to them. The witch was bitterly jealous and hated her stepdaughter more than ever; she bided her time and one day, when no one was about, she turned the young woman into a lynx and drove her into the dark forest. She put her own daughter in her place, dressed her in the stepdaughter's clothes, and managed it all so cleverly that neither the husband nor the servants noticed the deception. Only the old nurse understood. She was afraid to say anything, but as soon as the baby was hungry she carried it to the forest and sang:

> *Lynx of the forest! Your baby is crying,*
> *Your baby is asking for food and drink.*

The lynx came, threw off its skin, laid it on the ground by a tree stump and fed the baby; afterwards, she put on the skin again and disappeared among the trees.

"Where does the nurse take the baby?" the father wondered. He watched the old woman as she went to the forest and saw the lynx come and throw off its skin. While the mother was suckling the baby, he stole up from behind the bushes, seized the lynx's skin, and set fire to it.

"There's a smell of smoke," said the lynx. "I believe my skin is burning!"

"No," the nurse answered, "it must be the woodcutters lighting a bonfire."

The skin was burned, and the young woman returned to her home. She told her husband all that had happened, and as soon as their neighbors heard of it they gathered together, seized the witch and her daughter, and put them both to death.

The Cock, the Cat,
and the Fox

There was an old man who had a cat and a cock.* The cat grew tired of living with the old man and one day said to the cock: "Let's go to the forest—it's better there."

The cock said: "Very well," and off they went. They found an old hut in the forest and settled there. The cat went out hunting and the cock stayed at home and cooked the dinner.

One morning after the cat had gone out, Mrs. Fox walked past the hut and smelled the cock. The door was shut and the cock was nowhere to be seen, so she sat down by the window and sang:

> *Little cockerel, young and bold,*
> *Cock with a comb of gold,*
> *Glossy feathers on your head*
> *And a beard fine as silk,*
> *Look and see, here is some bread,*
> *Here is porridge made with milk!*

* The cock (in Russian *Petuh*) is called Petya in folk tales—a diminutive of Peter.

The cock wondered who it could be, singing so nicely; he opened the window, looked out, and the fox instantly seized him and carried him away.

The cock was frightened and cried with all his might:

> *The fox is taking me*
> *Through forest and lea*
> *Beyond the blue sea,*
> *Over mountains gray*
> *To foreign lands*
> *Far, far away.*
> *Brother cat, save me!*

Fortunately the cat was not far away; he heard the cock and rushed in pursuit. The fox saw him, let go the cock, and ran away. The cock and the cat returned to their hut.

The following day the cat went hunting again. "Mind, Petya," he said, "don't take any notice of what the fox says. If you open the window, she will carry you off again, and I may be out of earshot this time."

As soon as the cat had gone, Mrs. Fox arrived. She settled by the window and sang:

> *Little cockerel, young and bold,*
> *Cock with a comb of gold,*
> *Silken beard, glossy head,*
> *Look and see what a spread—*
> *Peas in plenty, new and old!*

The cock badly wanted some peas. Yet he would not open the window, remembering what the cat had said. But the fox went on singing and at last his resolution broke down. He looked out and the fox seized and carried him off. Again the cock began calling for the cat to save him. The cat had gone further afield than the day before, but he heard and arrived in time to rescue the cock.

When they came home, the cat said: "Look here, Petya, you really must do as you are told! I warned you about the fox, and yet you opened the window and peeped out. If you do it tomorrow, it will be the end of you, for I shall be nowhere near."

"Of course I won't peep out," said the cock. "I'm not so silly as all that."

In the morning the cat went off, and as soon as he was out of sight, Mrs. Fox appeared and began to sing. She sang about the milk porridge and the peas and about corn spilled by the road-side, but the cock was firm. He strutted about the hut saying to

himself: "I won't look out, I won't look out." Then Mrs. Fox
began a new song:

> *Close upon the forest edge*
> *Stands a dainty little sledge.*
> *Of itself it goes uphill,*
> *Up or down, as you will.*

"What kind of sledge can it be?" the cock wondered. "I'll just
have a peep."

As soon as he opened the window, the fox pounced upon him.
He cried and cried and called the cat, but it was no use—the cat
was too far away to hear. The fox carried him to a thicket of fir
trees, and there made a good meal of him.

When the cat came home, he found the door shut. He knocked
and called, but there was no answer. He walked around and saw
that the window was open and there was no one inside. He went to
look for Petya and presently found some feathers under a pine tree.
He guessed what had happened and wept bitterly.

The cat felt lonely without the cock and decided to return to his
master. The old man was delighted to see him and the cat never
deserted him again.

The Lame Duck

There once lived an old man and his wife who had no children. The old man made bark shoes, and the old woman spun.

One day they went mushrooming, and as they walked along they saw a nest under some bushes, and in the nest there was a pretty little duck. "Let's take it home," said the old woman.

They picked up the duck carefully, brought it home with them, and the old man made a soft cosy nest for it under a bench.

The following day the husband and wife went mushrooming again and when they came home they found that everything in the room had been put in order; the bowls and dishes had been washed and put on the shelf, and the towel was hung up to dry.

"Someone has been at work here," they said.

They went and asked their neighbor if she had seen anyone go into their cottage; but the neighbor said she had sat dozing on the doorstep and had seen no one.

The next day the old man and his wife went mushrooming once more. When they came home they saw that the table had been set for dinner, and there was a pot of hot cabbage soup ready and a loaf of freshly baked bread.

"Someone came and cooked our dinner for us," they said. They came out into the village street and asked another neighbor if she had seen anyone go into their cottage.

"Yes," she said, "I saw a girl coming in with two buckets of water from the well. Such a pretty girl, but just a little lame."

The following morning the husband and wife set out as though they meant to go mushrooming, but instead they hid behind a corner and watched to see if anyone would go into their hut. All of a sudden they saw that a beautiful girl came out of the door carrying two empty buckets on a yoke and went toward the well.

As soon as she had gone, the old people rushed in. They saw that the nest was in its place, but the duck had disappeared. So they seized the nest with all the feathers that were in it and threw it into the fire.

Presently the girl came back with the water from the well. She was alarmed at finding the old people at home and rushed to the nest—but the nest and the feathers had gone! She sat down and wept bitterly.

The old man and the old woman tried to comfort her and said they would look after her as their own daughter and love her dearly.

"No," said the girl. "I would have stayed and been as a daughter to you if you hadn't burnt my feathers and taken away my wings, but now I don't want to stay with you. Make me a distaff and spindle, old man, and I will go away."

The old man made a distaff and spindle for her, and she sat on a bench in the courtyard spinning flax.

A flock of wild ducks flew by. They saw the girl and called: "Why, there she is! Come and fly with us—we'll throw down some feathers to you."

But the girl said: "No, I will not fly with you: when I was in the meadow and broke my leg, you abandoned me and flew away."

Each duck threw down a feather to her and flew on.

Presently another flock of wild ducks came along. They, too, recognized the girl, asked her to join them, and threw down some

feathers for her. She collected all the feathers, dressed herself in them, turned into a duck, and flew away.

And the old man and his wife were left alone.

The Ram
and the Goat

A peasant said to his wife one day: "Let's drive away our ram and our goat; they eat a lot and are no use to us," and he turned them out. They took a bag with them and set out early in the morning to look for a place where they could settle. As they walked along, they found a wolf's head lying on the ground; the goat picked it up and put it into their bag.

In the evening they saw the light of a bonfire at the edge of the forest and thought they might get some supper there. But when they came near, they found three wolves sitting around the fire, cooking porridge. It was too late to draw back, so the ram and the goat wished the wolves good evening and asked if they might join them. "Yes," answered the wolves, "and when we have eaten our porridge, we'll eat you for our second course."

The ram trembled with fear, but the goat put a bold face on it and said: "Well, meanwhile let's have supper. Give me a wolf's head, brother ram."

The ram drew the wolf's head out of the bag.

"No," said the goat, "find a bigger one."

The ram put the head back into the bag and pulled it out again.

"No," said the goat, "this one is too small, get another. There are plenty to choose from."

When the wolves heard this, they felt distinctly uneasy; they had never before seen a ram with a bagful of wolves' heads slung over his shoulder. One of the wolves said: "I think I'll go and gather some dry sticks—the fire doesn't seem to burn well," and off he went to the forest.

After a time the second wolf said: "He is a long time gathering those sticks, I'd better go and help him"—and he also went away.

"I wonder what those two are doing," said the third wolf. "I'll go and tell them to hurry up"—and he, too, made for the forest. .

The goat and the ram were very glad to be left alone. They ate the wolves' porridge and decided to spend the night in a tree for safety. They helped each other to climb up among the branches and went to sleep.

When the three wolves met together in the forest, they felt rather foolish at having run away from a goat and a ram. "They couldn't have done anything to the three of us," they said. "Let's go and fight them."

They soon found the tree in which the goat and the ram had taken shelter, and settled under it waiting for them to come down. As soon as it was light, the ram woke up and the first thing he saw was the three wolves snapping their teeth at him. He trembled at the sight and, losing his balance, fell right on top of the big wolf nearest to the tree. The goat saw what had happened and called out from his branch: "That's right! Bring me the biggest!"

The wolf was so frightened when he heard this that he jumped up and ran away as fast as his legs would carry him, and his two comrades followed suit.

Kuzmá
Get-Rich-Quick

Young Kuzmá lived all alone in a dense, dark forest; all he had
was a small cottage, five hens, and a cock. One day he went out
hunting, and a fox, whose home was nearby, saw him go, ran to his
cottage, and ate one of the hens. When he came back, Kuzmá
found the hen was missing and thought that a hawk had carried it
off. The following day he went out again, and the fox met him in
the forest. "Where are you going to, dear Kuzmá?" she asked.

"A-hunting, Foxy."

"Then good-by for the present," the fox said, and she ran
straight to the cottage and carried off another hen.

When Kuzmá came home, another hen was missing. "I wonder
if Mrs. Fox has done this," he thought. So the next day, before
going out, he shut all the windows and the door. The fox met him
again and inquired where he was going, and as soon as she heard
that he was going hunting, she went straight to his cottage. But
Kuzmá turned back and followed her. The fox walked around the
cottage; all the windows and the door were shut tight. The clever
creature then clambered onto the roof and dropped down the
chimney. Kuzmá burst into the room and caught her.

"Aha!" he said, "you are the thief that steals my hens! Well, my dear madam, you won't come out of here alive!"

"Don't kill me, dear Kuzmá! I'll make you rich in no time—only please roast a hen for me in plenty of butter."

Kuzmá agreed; the fox had a lovely dinner and went to roll on the grass in the king's* private meadows.

A wolf ran past and said: "You must have had a good meal, you wily fox! Where, I wonder?"

"Oh, cousin wolf, I've been to dinner with the king. But surely you've been invited too? There was quite a crowd of us there— foxes and martens and sables and all kinds of animals."

"Couldn't you take me, too, to dine with the king, Foxy?" the wolf asked.

"Very well, but you must bring with you a thousand other wolves—the king wouldn't take the trouble to feast you alone."

The wolf called together a thousand wolves and the fox took them to the king, saying that it was a present from Kuzmá Get-Rich-Quick. The king was very pleased and had all the wolves put into an enclosure.

The next day Mrs. Fox asked Kuzmá to roast one more hen for her; she ate it with much relish and again went to roll about on the grass in the king's private meadows.

A bear walked past and said: "I see you've done yourself well, you crafty fox! Where have you been?"

"I've been to the king's banquet, Bruin. There were many animals there, and some are still feasting. You know what greedy beasts wolves are—they simply can't tear themselves away from their dinner."

"Couldn't you take me, too, to dine with the king, my dear?" the bear asked.

---

* The word "king" used here and in subsequent tales stands for "Tsar" or "Czar" which denotes the supreme ruler of Russia and also kings mentioned in the Bible, ancient history, folklore and Moslem or heathen rulers. The Russian word for European kings is *Korol*, probably derived from Carolus—Charlemagne. "Tsarevitch" means the Tsar's son and "Tsarevna," the Tsar's daughter.

The fox consented, but told him to bring with him a thousand bears, for the king would not think it worthwhile to hold a banquet for Bruin alone.

Bruin called together a thousand bears and they all followed the fox to the palace. They waited in the yard while the fox went to the king and asked him to accept all the bears as a gift from Kuzmá Get-Rich-Quick. The king sent his thanks to Kuzmá and had all the bears put into an enclosure.

Mrs. Fox again ran to Kuzmá's hut and begged him to roast for her the remaining hen and the cock. She thoroughly enjoyed her dinner and went to the king's private meadows to roll about on the lush green grass. A sable and a marten happened to go past and when they saw the fox, they said: "You must have had a grand meal, you sly fox! Where did you get it?"

"Ah, you know I am in great favor with the king. He is holding a feast today for all kinds of animals, and I must say I did myself well. There was an enormous crowd there. You know what greedy creatures wolves are—it's as though they'd never had enough to eat—and they are still gobbling. And the bears have gorged themselves till they can scarcely breathe!"

"Please, good Mrs. Fox, take us, too, to the palace! If only to have a look."

The fox agreed, told them to collect a thousand sables and martens, and led them all to the king, saying it was a present from Kuzmá Get-Rich-Quick. The king marveled at Kuzmá's wealth and was very pleased with his gift.

The following day the fox came to the king again and said: "Your Majesty, Kuzmá Get-Rich-Quick sends you his compliments and asks you to lend him a bushel measure. He has to measure some silver coins, and his own bushels are all taken up with gold."

The king gave a bushel measure to Mrs. Fox at once. She took it to Kuzmá and told him to measure sand with it till the measure looked shiny on one side. Then he stuck a few silver coins in the seams. In the morning she carried the measure back to the king and inquired if he would be willing to give his daughter to Kuzmá

in marriage. The king did not refuse, but said that he and the princess would like to meet Kuzmá, and invited him to come and see them the following day.

Mrs. Fox reflected that although Kuzmá was a good-looking lad, he was not smart enough, and indeed his coat was distinctly shabby. So when he set out for the palace the next day, she ran in front of him to a bridge which lay on his way and engaged some workmen to saw down the posts. As soon as Kuzmá set foot on the bridge it gave way, and he fell into the water. The fox made a fearful to-do and rushed about crying that Kuzmá Get-rich-Quick was drowning. The king heard and immediately sent his men to rescue Kuzmá and provide him with suitable clothes; and when Kuzmá eventually appeared before the king and the princess, he looked so handsome that the marriage was agreed upon at once and celebrated the next day.

Kuzmá stayed for a week or two with his father-in-law, and then the king said to him: "Well, my dear son-in-law, now let us go and have a look at your house."

There was no way to get out of it, so Kuzmá had to make ready. The carriage was brought and they set off. Mrs. Fox ran on a good way in front. Presently she saw a large flock of sheep and asked the shepherds who owned it. "King Serpent," they answered. "Tell everyone," the fox said, "that the sheep belong to Kuzmá Get-Rich-Quick, or else King Fire and Queen Lightning who are coming along will burn you to death."

The shepherds were frightened and promised to do as they were told. The fox ran on, and seeing a huge herd of pigs, asked: "Whose herd is it?" "King Serpent's," answered the swineherds. "Tell everyone that it is Kuzmá Get-Rich-Quick's; if you don't, King Fire and Queen Lightning who will soon be here will burn you to death." The swineherds were frightened and promised to do as they were told.

After this, the fox came to a herd of cows, and then to a drove of camels which also belonged to King Serpent, and gave the same

orders to the cowherds and the camel drivers. At last she reached
King Serpent's fine white stone palace and ran straight in.

"What news, Foxy?" asked the serpent.

"Bad news, King Serpent! You must make haste and hide yourself. The dread King Fire and Queen Lightning are coming and
burning up everything on their way! They've burned up all your
flocks and herds—the sheep and the pigs, and the cows, and the
camels. I rushed off at once to tell you and was nearly choked with
smoke on my way here!"

The serpent was greatly troubled and asked in fear:

"Whatever shall I do, Foxy?"

"There's an old oak tree in your garden, all hollow inside: go and
hide in it, until they have driven past your palace."

The serpent lost no time and hid himself in the hollow oak tree
as the fox suggested.

Meanwhile Kuzmá Get-Rich-Quick drove on and on with his
wife and father-in-law. They reached the flock of sheep and the
princess asked the shepherds whose flock it was. "Kuzmá Get-Rich-
Quick's," they answered. The king was very pleased: "You have a
lot of sheep, dear son-in-law."

They came to the herd of swine, and the princess asked who
owned it. "Kuzmá Get-Rich-Quick," the swineherds answered.

"You have a lot of pigs, dear son-in-law," remarked the king.

When they came to the herd of cows and then of camels they
were told that it all belonged to Kuzmá Get-Rich-Quick.

When they reached King Serpent's palace, the fox came out
onto the steps to greet them and led them in. The king marveled at
the splendor of the place and at the sumptuous meal that was waiting for them on the table.

After dinner they went into the garden, and Kuzmá, prompted
by the fox, suggested that the king and he should amuse themselves by shooting arrows at the hollow in the oak tree, and see who
was the better shot. Between them they soon killed the serpent
who lay coiled there, afraid to stir.

Kuzmá established himself in the serpent's kingdom and lived there happily with his young wife to the end of his days. They treated Mrs. Fox to a roast fowl every day, and she stayed with them till there were no more fowls left.

The Dog
and the Cock

A peasant had a very bad harvest, and could no longer feed his
dog and his cock—which were all the livestock he possessed.

So the dog said to the cock:

"You know, Petya, I think we'll find more to eat in the forest
than here."

"That's true enough," said the cock. "We may as well go away."
So they said good-by to their master and went off in search of a
new home. They walked all day without finding anything suitable,
and as it began to grow dark the cock said:

"Let's spend the night in a tree. I'll roost on a branch, and you
can sleep in the hollow at the bottom. It won't be too bad."

The cock flew up to a branch, tucked his feet under him, and
went to sleep. The dog made himself a bed in the hollow.

They had a good night, and at dawn the cock woke up as usual
and crowed for all the forest to hear:

Cockle-doodle-do! Wake up, all of you!
Soon the day will have begun,
Wake and greet the rising sun!

A fox, asleep in its home nearby, woke up with a start. "Why, there's a cock crowing in the forest! What is he doing here? He must have lost his way. He'll provide a fine dinner for me!"

Mrs. Fox went to look for the cock and saw him on a branch close by. She walked up to the tree and said:

"What a lovely cock! I don't believe I've ever seen such a beauty! Your feathers shine like gold, your tail is simply beyond description. And such a beautiful voice! I could never grow tired of listening to it. Dear little cock, come down and let's make friends! As it happens, there's a christening at my house today, so there are plenty of good things to eat. Come along!"

"All right, I'll come," said the cock, "only you must invite my friend as well. We go everywhere together."

"And where is your friend?"

"Down below, in the tree hollow."

Mrs. Fox thought the friend was another cock and thrust her head into the hollow—but the dog went "snap" and bit her nose!

Master Frost

There once lived an old man and an old woman with their three daughters. The eldest was the old woman's stepdaughter and she treated her very badly. She scolded the poor girl from morning till night and made her do all the work: Marfa had to get up before daybreak, and fetch water, and bring in the logs, and heat the stove, and sweep the floor, and give fodder to the cattle. She worked all day long, yet the old woman was never satisfied and kept grumbling that things were not done properly. Marfa was a good girl and did not answer back or complain, but tried to do her best to please the stepmother and her daughters. The girls followed their mother's example and were as unkind to Marfa as could be; they often made her cry, and nothing pleased them better. Her father was sorry for her, but he could do nothing: he was old, his wife was a shrew, and his stepdaughters were lazy and bad-tempered. Everyone in the village knew what they were like, and no suitors presented themselves to seek them in marriage—while Marfa was much sought after.

The old woman believed that if she could get rid of Marfa, her own daughters would have a better chance of finding husbands, so she thought of a plan. One evening she said to her husband: "Get up early tomorrow, have the sledge ready, and take Marfa with you; and you, my girl, pack your belongings and put on clean clothes—you'll go on a visit with your father."

Marfa was very glad, and in the morning, after she had washed herself and said her prayers, she packed her things and dressed in her best. Her father got up very early, and by the time he had harnessed the horse she was quite ready for the journey.

"If you are ready, both of you, come and eat your breakfast," shouted the stepmother, putting on the table a bowl of last night's cabbage soup and a loaf of black bread. "And mind you be quick."

They had not finished their meal when she said:

"Old man, I want you to take Marfa to her bridegroom. Go first along the road and then turn to the right toward the pine forest. Right in the middle of it there's a big pine tree at the top of the hill; leave her there to be married to Master Frost. I've had enough of her, I don't want to set my eyes on her again."

Her husband stared at her, and poor Marfa burst into tears. "No, don't you snivel!" snapped the old woman. "Your bridegroom is a fine gentleman and rich as a king. All the snow-clad pine trees and firs and birches are his, and all the ice on ponds and rivers."

The old man stood up without a word and took his daughter's box to the sledge. Then he told her to put on her coat and they set off.

It was a long way to the forest and the day was far spent by the time they reached it. The old man drove right through the thickets to the big pine tree on the hill; there he took Marfa's box out of the sledge, put it under the tree and told her to wait for her bridegroom. He went home with a heavy heart, thinking that he would never see his daughter again.

The girl sat on the box, shivering with cold. Presently she heard Master Frost cracking the branches, jumping from tree to tree and coming nearer and nearer. He got onto the pine tree under which she sat and called to her from the top:

"Are you warm, fair maiden? Are you warm, my beauty?"

"Quite warm, Master Frost, thank you kindly."

Frost came lower down, cracking the branches more loudly.

"Are you warm, fair maiden? Are you warm, my beauty?"

The girl could scarcely breathe, but still she said:

"Yes, Master Frost, thank you kindly."

Master Frost came quite close to her, making the branches crack louder than ever.

"Are you warm, fair maiden? Are you warm, my beauty?"

The girl was freezing to death and could only just whisper:

"Warmth is from God, dear Frost, and the cold is from Him too."

Then Frost had pity on her, wrapped her up in furs and rugs, and restored her to life.

In the morning the old woman sent her husband to the forest. She wanted to make sure that Marfa was dead. He harnessed the horse and drove to the big pine tree, expecting the worst. Great was his joy when he saw his daughter alive and well, dressed in a beautiful fur coat and a rich bridal veil, and beside her a silver-clad box filled with splendid presents. He wasted no time in asking questions but put everything on the sledge and merrily drove Marfa home.

The stepmother was astonished when she saw her safe and sound and dressed in such finery. The next day she said to the old man: "Tomorrow you must take my daughters, too, to the forest! They'll bring home better presents than your Marfa."

Early in the morning she gave a good breakfast to her daughters and dressed them up as though for a wedding. The old man took them to the forest and left them under the big pine tree on the hill. The girls sat there laughing. "A queer fancy Mother has of finding husbands for us in the forest! As though there weren't young men in the village!"

They had thick fur coats on, and yet they began to feel chilly. "I have shivers down my back," said one. "What if the suitors don't come? We shall freeze to death here."

"And what if only one comes?" said the other. "Which of us will he choose?"

"It certainly won't be you, you silly!"

"Not likely to choose you, is he?"

And they began quarreling.

Meanwhile Master Frost came to the treetops making the branches crack. The girls fancied it was the sound of a sledge driving up.

"Hush, he's coming, and there are bells on his sledge," said the elder. Frost was coming nearer and nearer. He settled on the top of the pine tree under which the girls sat, and bending down, asked them:

"Are you warm, fair maidens? Are you warm, my beauties?"

"We're horribly cold, Frost! We are waiting for a bridegroom and he doesn't come, perdition take him!"

Master Frost came lower down, making the branches crack louder and louder.

"Are you warm, fair maidens? Are you warm, my beauties?"

"Oh, curse you, leave us alone! Can't you see we are stiff and numb with cold?"

Frost came down still lower and sent such a cold blast through them that they instantly froze to death.

In the morning the old woman said: "Harness the horse, man, and put plenty of hay and some rugs in the sledge. I expect the girls are pretty cold—there was a terrible frost last night. And don't you dawdle over your breakfast."

The old man drove straight to the big pine tree and found that both girls were frozen. He brought the bodies home, and when his wife saw that her daughters were dead she flew at her husband, beside herself with fury, blaming him for what had happened. "It was no fault of mine, you crazy woman!" he said. "It was your own greed and envy that made you send the girls to their death in the forest."

The old woman stormed for a time, but eventually made peace with her husband. Meanwhile Marfa married a good young man in the village and they lived all their life in peace and contentment.

A Swift Messenger

There was once a poor peasant who had three sons. They lived on the edge of an enormous marsh which stretched for hundreds of miles; there was no way across it, and to drive round it took well over a year. So one day the peasant said to his sons: "Let us do a good service to our fellow Christians and make a road across the marsh!"

They set to work and, after many months of toil, succeeded in making a good road and building a bridge over the bog, so that now it took only three weeks to walk across it and only three days to ride. When all the work was finished the old man said to his eldest son, Ivan: "Go and sit under the bridge and find out whether people speak well or ill about us."

Ivan went and hid himself under the bridge. Two old pilgrims walked over it and said one to the other: "The man who made the road and built this bridge may ask of the Lord anything he likes, and the Lord will give it him."

As soon as Ivan heard these words, he came out from his hiding place and said: "I made the road and built this bridge together with my father and my brothers."

"What would you ask of the Lord?" said the old men.

"I wish the Lord would give me enough money to last me a lifetime."

"Very well, go to the open field in which there stands a solitary oak tree; under that oak there is a deep cave, and in the cave there is plenty of gold and silver and precious stones. Take a spade and dig, and the Lord will give you enough to last you a lifetime."

Ivan went to the field, dug out a lot of gold and si'ver and precious stones from under the oak, and took it home.

"Well, my son," the old man asked him, "have you seen anyone walk or drive over the bridge, and what do people say about us?"

Ivan told his father about the two old pilgrims and of the riches with which they rewarded him.

On the following day the old man sent to the bridge his second son, Vassili. He too hid himself so as to overhear all that passers-by might say. Two old pilgrims walked across the bridge and said one to the other:

"If the man who made this road and built this bridge asks anything of the Lord, the Lord will give it to him."

As soon as Vassili heard these words he came out of his hiding place and said to the pilgrims: "It was I who made the road and built this bridge together with my father and my brothers."

"What would you ask of God?"

"I wish the Lord would provide me with bread all my life long."

"Very well. Go home, make a clearing in the forest, plow it, and sow the seed: the Lord will give you enough bread to last you a lifetime."

Vassili went home, told his father all that the pilgrims had said, and followed their advice.

On the third day the old man sent his third son, Semyon-the-young-lad. He concealed himself under the bridge and listened. Two old pilgrims came along; when they reached his hiding place one said to the other:

"The man who made this road and built this bridge may ask of the Lord whatever he will, and the Lord will give it to him."

Semyon-the-young-lad heard their words, came toward them, and said: "It was I who built this bridge together with my father and my brothers."

"What would you ask of the Lord?"

"The favor I ask of God is that He should let me serve our gracious king as a soldier."

"Ask for something else! A soldier's lot is a hard one; if you are a soldier, you will fall prisoner to the Sea King and shed many a tear."

"You are old and wise—surely you know that if a man sheds no tears in this life, he will have to weep in the world to come."

"Well, if you are so determined to serve the king, we give you our blessing!" said the pilgrims. They laid their hands on Semyon and turned him into a light-footed deer. The deer ran all the way to its home and back again to the pilgrims, who turned it into a hare. The hare ran all the way to its home and back again to the pilgrims, who turned it into a tiny golden-feathered bird. The bird flew to its home, perched on the window, and returned to the pilgrims who gave it human form again.

"Now, Semyon-the-young-lad, you may go into the king's service," they said. "If you have to go somewhere in a hurry, you can turn into a deer, a hare, and a bird—we have taught you how."

Semyon-the-young-lad came home and asked his father to let him go to be a soldier.

"A soldier, indeed! You are much too young," his father said.

"Please let me go, Father; it is God's will."

At last the old man gave him leave to go; Semyon said good-by to him and to his brothers and set off on his journey.

There is no telling how long he was on the way, but at last he reached the capital and went straight to the king. "Be not angry with me, gracious king, but allow me to ask a favor," he said.

"What is it, lad?" asked the king.

"Let me serve you as a soldier, Your Majesty!"

"Why, you are not fit to be a soldier—you are much too young."

"I may be young and foolish, but please God, I will serve you no worse than others."

The king granted the young lad's request, and kept him as his personal attendant.

After a while an infidel ruler declared war against the Christians. The king collected an army and set out to meet the enemy; Semyon-the-young-lad would not be left behind, so the king took him to the war. They were months and months on the march and passed through a number of foreign countries; at last they drew near to the enemy. In another three days they were to join battle, when suddenly the king discovered that he was without his battle-ax and his sharp sword—he had left them behind and now had nothing to defend himself with and no means of defeating the enemy. He made a proclamation throughout his army that whosoever could run back to the palace and fetch the sword and the battle-ax, would have the king's daughter, Princess Marya, for wife and half the kingdom, and be made heir to the throne. Several men volunteered; one said he could bring the sword and the battle-ax in three years' time, another that he could do it in two years, a third one in a year. Semyon-the-young-lad said to the king: "Your Majesty, I can do your errand in three days' time." The king was overjoyed; he took Semyon by the hand, kissed him, and at once wrote a letter to Princess Marya saying that she was to give the messenger the sword and the battle-ax. Semyon took the letter and set out on his journey.

After walking for a mile, he turned into a light-footed deer, swift as an arrow; when he was tired out, he changed into a hare and went on running with renewed vigor; when he was thoroughly exhausted, he changed into a golden-feathered bird and flew swifter then he had run. In a day and a half he reached the king's palace. He changed into a man again, went in, and gave Princess Marya the king's letter. She read it and was greatly surprised. "How did you manage to cover all that distance in so short a time?"

"This is how I did it," said the messenger and turned into a deer. It ran round the room, came to Princess Marya, and rested its head

on her lap; she took out a pair of scissors and cut off some of its
hair. The deer turned into a hare, skipped about the room, and
jumped onto the princess' lap; she cut some fur off its head. The
hare turned into a tiny golden-feathered bird; the bird flew about
the room and perched on the princess' hand. Princess Marya cut a
few golden feathers off its head and put them together with the
deer hair and the hare's fur in a handkerchief which she carefully
hid away. The bird turned into the messenger. The princess gave
him food and drink, fitted him out for the journey, and gave him
her father's sword and battle-ax. Then they kissed each other good-
by and Semyon-the-young-lad started on his return journey. Again
he first ran as a deer, then as a hare, and then flew as a bird. To-

ward the end of the third day he saw the king's encampment. Within some two hundred yards of it he lay down to rest on the seashore, by a willow bush, and put the sword and the battle-ax by his side. He was so tired that he instantly dropped fast asleep.

One of the army generals happened to walk past. He saw the messenger, pushed him over into the sea, and carried off the sword and the battle-ax. He took them to the king and said:

"Here is your sword, Your Majesty, and your battle-ax. I've been to fetch them myself, for that boaster Semyon-the-young-lad would take a good three years on the journey."

The King thanked him, made ready for the battle, and in a short time completely overcame the enemy.

The moment that Semyon-the-young-lad fell into the water, the Sea King caught him and carried him to the bottom of the sea. He lived there for a whole year, and at last he could bear it no longer and fell to weeping. The Sea King asked: "Do you find it lonely here, Semyon-the-young-lad?"

"Very lonely, Your Majesty."

"Would you like to go back to the world of men?"

"I would, if you will let me."

The Sea King brought him ashore in the dead of the night and went back into the sea. Semyon-the-young-lad prayed fervently for daylight, but just before sunrise the Sea King came out, seized him, and carried him to the bottom of the sea again.

Another year passed, and the same thing happened—the Sea King took pity on Semyon's tears and brought him ashore at midnight, but snatched him back before it was daylight. A third year passed, and Semyon-the-young-lad wept more bitterly than ever. Again the Sea King offered to give him a breath of the world of men, took him ashore, and went back into the sea. Semyon prayed with tears for the sun to rise and, behold, the sun rose suddenly in all its glory. The Sea King did not venture to come out of water in broad daylight and the lad was freed from his power.

He set off at once for his native land. He turned into a deer and ran swift as an arrow till he could run no more; then he changed into a hare and then into a little bird, and in less than three days reached the palace of his king.

The king meanwhile had betrothed his daughter, Princess Marya, to the treacherous general, and they were to be married on the very day that Semyon-the-young-lad came back. He walked into the wedding hall, and as soon as the bride saw him, she said to her father: "May it please Your Majesty, my true bridegroom is not the one who is sitting at the table, but the one who has just come in! Show us, Semyon-the-young-lad, how you brought the sword and the battle-ax," she added.

Semyon turned into a deer which ran across the room and laid its head on the princess' lap. She took out of her kerchief the deer's hair and showed her father where she had cut it off. The deer turned into a hare and after scampering about the room jumped into the princess' lap; she showed the king the piece of hare's fur she had cut off. The hare turned into a little bird which flew about the room and perched on the princess' hand. She untied a knot in her kerchief and showed the golden feathers she had cut off. Thus the king learned the truth of the matter. He was very angry with the wicked general and had him banished so far that he was never heard of again. Princess Marya married Semyon-the-young-lad, whom the king made his heir, and they lived in peace and happiness.

The Brown Cow

There once lived a man and wife, and they had a lovely young daughter Marya. The wife died, and the man married another woman, called Yagíshna. She had three daughters of her own; the eldest had only one eye, the second had two eyes, and the third had three. Yagíshna took a dislike to Marya; she dressed her in rags, gave her only black bread to eat, and sent her out at dawn to tend the brown cow.

Every morning Marya took the cow to the far-off meadow, and as soon as they reached it, she climbed into the cow's right ear, came out of the left ear, and found plenty of food and drink set before her, and a beautiful dress to wear. She would spend the day like a lady, but at sunset she put on her old clothes again and drove the cow home. She broke up and gave to the birds the chunk of black bread which her stepmother gave her for dinner, but once or twice she forgot to do so and brought the bread back with her. Yagíshna wondered what the girl could have had to eat during the day, and sent her eldest daughter, One-Eye, to spy on Marya.

They came to the meadow; it was a hot summer's day, and One-Eye, not used to walking, was tired out. "Lie down and have a rest, sister," said Marya, and One-Eye was only too glad to stretch herself on the soft green grass. Marya began to sing, "Sleep, sister, sleep! One eye, close yourself!" And the sister soon fell asleep. Then Marya climbed into the cow's right ear, came out of the left one, and found a good meal spread before her and a splendid gown to put on. At sunset she dressed in her tattered clothes once more and woke her sister. One-Eye was greatly distressed at having slept so long and seen nothing, for she knew that her mother would be angry with her. When they came home, Yagíshna asked her: "What had Marya to eat and to drink?" One-Eye could not say, and Yagíshna scolded her.

The following morning Yagíshna sent her second daughter, Two-Eyes, to watch Marya. As soon as they came to the meadow, Two-Eyes lay down on the grass, for she was hot and tired. Marya sang to her, "Sleep, sister, sleep! Two eyes, close yourselves!" And the sister dropped fast asleep. Then Marya climbed into the brown cow's right ear, came out of the left ear, and found an excellent dinner waiting for her and a fine dress to wear. Two-Eyes slept all day, and when at sunset Marya wakened her, it was time to go home. Again Yagíshna could find out nothing from her daughter.

On the third morning she sent Three-Eyes to spy on Marya. The two girls came to the green meadow and when Three-Eyes lay down to rest, Marya sang to her, "Sleep, sister, sleep! One eye, close yourself, second eye, close yourself!" But she forgot about the third eye. So while two eyes slept, the third watched all that Marya did. She went up to the brown cow, climbed into its right ear, came out of the left, and found a table spread with the daintiest food and a gorgeous dress to put on. At sunset, clad in her old rags, she roused Three-Eyes and they walked home. Yagíshna asked her daughter: "Well, what does Marya eat and drink?" and Three-Eyes told her all that she had seen with her third eye.

Yagíshna called for the cook and said to him: "Kill the brown cow, old man."

Marya heard this and begged the man to give her a piece of the cow's guts. He threw her a bit and she went and planted it by the

garden gate. Within three days there grew out of it a slender tree with silver leaves and sweet red berries. Songbirds of every kind nested in the tree, singing so beautifully that people gathered at the gate to listen.

One day a handsome young prince came riding by. He stopped to look at the wonderful tree and caught sight of Marya in the garden. So he said to the mistress of the house: "I will marry the maiden who gathers a bowlful of these lovely berries for me." Yagíshna thought this would be a fine opportunity for one of her daughters and sent One-Eye to gather the berries. But the branches drew away from her when she tried to take hold of them, and the

birds very nearly pecked out her only eye. The same thing happened when Two-Eyes and Three-Eyes tried to pluck the fruit, so
there was nothing for it but to let Marya do it. When she came to
the tree, the branches bent down of themselves toward her, and
the birds came and put into her bowl two berries for every one that
she picked. She presented the fruit to the prince, and he was so
enchanted with her that they were married that same day and lived
happily ever after.

Marko the Rich
and Vassili the Luckless

There once lived a merchant known as Marko the Rich. He was a proud and hardhearted man, feared and disliked by everyone. His wealth was immense, but he never gave a penny to the poor, and if a beggar came to his gates he set his dogs at him.

One bitterly cold winter evening two old pilgrims begged him for a night's shelter. He wouldn't hear of it, and shouting abuse at them, drove them away. A poor woman who lived next door took pity on them and asked them in. She had only one room and she was old and infirm, but she waited on the pilgrims, gave them supper, and made them as comfortable as she could. In the night she heard a tap on the window, and a voice said:

"A baby boy was born today in such and such a village. What name will you give him, and what is to be his lot in life?"

The pilgrims answered: "His name shall be Vassili the Luckless, and he is to inherit all the wealth of Marko the Rich."

When the woman woke up in the morning, she found that the pilgrims had gone and that she herself was a changed creature—all her infirmity had disappeared and she felt as though some twenty years had been taken off her age. She looked so young and well that

Marko the Rich could scarcely believe his eyes when she came to tell him of what she had heard in the night. He understood that the pilgrims were not ordinary men, and was much perturbed at the prospect of losing all his wealth to the newborn boy.

He decided to find out if there really was such a boy. He ordered his sledge and drove to the village. He went straight to the priest and asked him if on such and such a day a boy had been born in his parish.

"Yes," said the priest, "he was born in the poorest family in the village. I have named him Vassili, and his surname is Luckless, but I haven't yet christened him because no godparents can be found—his father is almost a beggar."

Marko volunteered to be godfather to the boy; he ordered a sumptuous dinner, and after the christening, the whole company feasted till evening. On the following morning he sent for the baby's father, and after talking to him very kindly, asked if he would give him the boy.

"I know you are a poor man," he said, "and find it hard to provide for your family as it is, and now this child will be a fresh burden to you. But I can bring him up in comfort, and give you some money to live on. Here is a thousand rubles—let me have the boy."

The father hesitated, but finally agreed to part with his son. Marko wrapped the baby in furs, put it in his sledge, and drove off.

After traveling a few miles, he stopped close to a deep ravine, gave his godson to the servant, and said: "Take the baby by the feet and fling it into the ravine." The servant did as he was told, and Marko muttered to himself, chuckling, "Now let him enjoy my riches out there in the snow!"

Three days afterward some merchants were traveling by the same road on their way to Marko the Rich to pay him twelve thousand rubles which they owed him. As they drew near the ravine, they heard a child's voice, and sent one of their servants to find out where it came from. The servant went down to the bottom of the ravine and saw a marvel: there was a green meadow, and a baby was sitting on the grass, playing with the flowers. The servant ran back and told his master what he had seen; the master went to see for himself, picked up the baby and, wrapping it in his fur coat, brought it back to the sledge and the party continued their journey.

When the merchants came to Marko's house he asked how it was they had a baby with them. They told him, and he understood at once that it was Vassili the Luckless, his godson. He gave his guests dinner and plenty to drink and began persuading them to leave the boy with him. They did not want to at first, for they had meant to adopt the foundling, but when Marko said he would remit their debt, they agreed and gave him the child.

Three days after they had gone, Marko put the boy into a barrel, sealed it, and threw it into the river.

The barrel floated down the river and the current brought it close to a monastery. A monk who had come to fetch water heard a baby crying and thought the sound came from the barrel. He got into a boat, caught the barrel and, bringing it ashore, broke it open —and indeed there was a child in it. He took it back with him to the monastery and the abbot named the child Vassili.

For eighteen years Vassili lived at the monastery; he was a good and intelligent boy and everyone loved him. He learned to sing in the choir, to read and to write, and the abbot made him his cellarer.

One day Marko the Rich set out on a long journey to collect debts that were owing to him. The monastery was on his way and, as was his wont, he stopped there for the night. He noticed the smart young cellarer and asked where he had come from. The abbot told him Vassili's story and was high in his praises of the young man. Marko understood at once that it was his godson and determined to destroy him. He pretended to take a kind interest in Vassili's future and said to the abbot: "It isn't fair to a fine lad like that to keep him cooped up in a monastery where he has no chance of bettering himself or seeing the world. If you would let him go into my service, I'd make a man of him."

The abbot loved Vassili and took the wicked Marko's words to heart. He consulted his monks and they all agreed that they ought not to stand in Vassili's way; so with many tears they parted from him and gave him their blessing to go with Marko.

As soon as Marko had Vassili in his power, he dispatched him with a letter he had written to his wife. The letter said: "As soon as you receive this, send the bearer to the foundry and tell the foreman to throw him into the cauldron of boiling metal. This young man is my bitterest enemy." The letter was sealed, and Vassili had no suspicion of what was in it. He walked along cheerfully, and before long met two old pilgrims who asked him where he was going. "I am going to the house of Marko the Rich with a letter to his wife."

"Give us the letter."

Vassili did as they asked, and after holding the letter in their hands for a minute or two, they gave it back to him and said: "Go in peace, all shall be well with you."

When Vassili reached his destination he asked for the lady of the house and gave her the letter. She was much surprised when she read it; it said "Wife! On receipt of this, give our daughter Anastasia in marriage to the bearer of this letter. Do so the very next day, and mind you carry out my command: such is my will." She called Anastasia and showed the letter both to her and to Vassili. The young people liked each other, and the wedding was celebrated the next day.

After a few weeks Marko the Rich returned from his travels. His wife went to meet him at the landing stage and took her daughter and son-in-law with her. When Marko saw them he was beside himself with fury. "How did you dare to marry our daughter to him?" he shouted at his wife. "Why, such were your orders," she answered, and showed him the letter. Marko read it and saw that it was written in his own hand.

A month passed, then another, then a third. Marko the Rich called his son-in-law and said to him: "You must go to a land at the back of the beyond, to the kingdom of King Dragon. Get from him the tribute he owes me for the last twelve years, and ask him what has become of my twelve ships that have been lost for three years. Set out tomorrow at the crack of dawn."

Vassili the Luckless got up very early the next morning, said his prayers, kissed his wife good-by, and taking a provision of rusks in his pockets, set out on his journey.

He walked through many a kingdom, and one day he heard a voice calling to him: "Vassili the Luckless, where are you going?" He looked around. "Who is speaking?"

"I, the oak tree, am asking you, where are you going?"

"To King Dragon, to collect twelve years' tribute."

"When you have a chance, ask him about me. I've stood here for three hundred years; how much longer have I to stand?" Vassili promised to ask and went on his way.

He walked on and on, and came to a big wide river. As he was being ferried across, the ferryman asked him where he was going. "To King Dragon, to collect twelve years' tribute."

"When you have a chance, ask about me. I've been on this ferry for thirty years; how much longer am I to stay here?"

"I'll ask," Vassili promised and went on his way.

He walked on and on and came to the deep blue sea. A whale lay across it, and people walked and drove along its back as though it were a bridge. When Vassili stepped on to it, the whale asked him: "Where are you going, Vassili the Luckless?"

"To King Dragon, to collect twelve years' tribute."

"When you have a chance, ask about me. Here I lie across the sea and people walk and drive across me so that my very ribs are laid bare; how much longer am I to serve as a bridge?"

"All right, I won't forget," said Vassili, and went on his way.

After many a day he came to a green meadow, and in it there stood a big palace. Vassili the Luckless went up the steps and walked from one splendidly furnished room to another, meeting no one. At last in the very farthest room he found a maiden who sat on the bed weeping bitterly. When she saw Vassili, she came for-

ward and asked who he was and why he had come into this evil place.

"I am called Vassili the Luckless, and I have been sent here by Marko the Rich to demand from King Dragon twelve years' tribute which he owes Marko."

"Ah, you luckless young man!" cried the maiden. "It isn't for tribute that Marko sent you here, but so that the Dragon might devour you! Well, I will try and save you. The Dragon is away just now, and before he comes back tell me how you have managed to find your way here."

Vassili told her all that had happened to him on the journey and repeated the questions that the oak tree, the ferryman, and the whale had asked him. While they were talking, a great whirlwind arose, the palace shook, and a loud roar was heard—it was King Dragon coming home. The maiden hastily hid Vassili under the bed and told him to keep quiet and listen to all that she and the Dragon might say.

"Fe-fi-fo-fum! I smell the blood of a Russian man! Who's been here?" he cried.

"Why, is it likely that anyone should come here!" said the maiden. "You have been flying over Russia and its smell is still in your nostrils."

"I am tired out," said the Dragon, and he stretched himself out on the bed. "Sit by me and talk or sing till I go to sleep." She sat down and said to the Dragon:

"I had such a queer dream last night. I dreamt I was walking along the road and an old tree called out to me, 'Ask the King how much longer am I to stand here?' "

"It is to stand until a young man comes and pushes it toward the east with his foot: then the oak will be uprooted and fall, and underneath there will be a mass of gold and silver—more than Marko the Rich has!" King Dragon said.

"Then I went on dreaming that I came to a big broad river and the ferryman asked me how long he must stay on the ferry and take people across."

"Not long. Let him put in his place the first man who comes, and push the ferry away from the bank; that man will be ferryman instead of him for ever and ever."

"And again I dreamt that I walked across the deep blue sea on the back of a whale, and the whale asked me how long it would have to lie there and serve as a bridge."

"It is to lie there till it disgorges Marko's twelve ships. As soon as it does, it will plunge into the sea and its ribs will be covered with flesh again and its whole body be sound."

After saying this, the Dragon dropped fast asleep. As soon as he began to snore, the maiden let Vassili the Luckless out of the palace. He thanked her and set out homeward.

He walked on and on, and came to the deep blue sea. The whale asked him: "Well, did you ask King Dragon about me?"

"I did. When I have crossed over to over the other side, I will tell you."

He crossed the sea and said: "Disgorge the twelve ships of Marko the Rich, and you'll be free."

The whale obeyed, and twelve ships sailed away, not in the least damaged. The waves rose so high that although Vassili had run far inland he found himself knee-deep in water.

He walked on and on, and came to the ferryman.

"Have you asked King Dragon about me?" he asked.

"I did."

"Well, what's his answer?"

"Ferry me across, and I'll tell you."

When Vassili was safely across, he said: "Put the first man who comes to you into your place, push the ferry away from the landing place, and go home!"

At last he reached the speaking oak and struck it eastward with his foot: the oak fell, and under its roots there was no end of gold and silver and precious stones. Vassili looked around and saw twelve ships—the very ones which the whale had disgorged—sailing toward the shore. The sailors carried all the treasure to the ships and sailed home, taking Vassili with them.

Word was sent to Marko the Rich that his son-in-law was coming home with twelve ships laden with gold. Marko was furious; he ordered his carriage and set out to consult the Dragon about how best to destroy Vassili. He came to the river and got onto the ferry. The ferryman pushed it off from the landing place, and Marko the Rich remained there forever, ferrying people across.

Meanwhile Vassili the Luckless joined his wife and his mother-in-law, and they lived happily ever afterward, helping the poor and befriending the fatherless and widows.

Straight and Crooked

In a certain village there lived two poor peasants. One was a good and upright man, and the other was thievish and deceitful; their neighbors nicknamed them Straight and Crooked.

One day the two men fell to disputing whether it was better to live honestly or by fraud. Neither would yield his point, and so they decided to go into the world together and, while seeking work, ask other people's opinion on the matter.

As they walked along, they saw a peasant serf plowing. "Godspeed you, brother!" they said. "Settle our dispute for us: is it better to make one's living by fair dealing or by crooked?"

"Fair dealing won't take you far in life, mates! Honesty doesn't pay. Take us serfs: our masters make us work so hard that the only way to get a respite is to sham illness."

"There—you see I was right," said Crooked.

The next person they met was a tradesman. They put the same question to him, and he said: "Oh, you can't make money unless you cheat. Honest people have no chance in life."

"I told you so," Crooked remarked.

The following day they saw a gentleman driving past. They took off their caps to him and asked if he would mind telling them if it was better to be honest and truthful or to live by trickery. "If you tell the truth and stand up for justice, you are sure to get into trouble," he answered.

Crooked thought he had won his point, but Straight said, "No, we ought to live in the way God bids us. Whatever happens to me, I will not cheat or tell lies."

They went on and on. Crooked did very well for himself; he knew how to get on the right side of people and they gave him food and drink, and provisions to take away with him. Straight was content to earn a piece of bread by working for it.

They came to a desolate tract of country; no habitation was in sight, nothing but wasteland on either side of the road. Straight grew very hungry and asked Crooked for a piece of bread.

"Yes, but what will you give me for it?"

"Take what you like."

"I will take your eye."

"Well, so be it."

Crooked put out his companion's left eye and gave him a small piece of bread.

Another day passed; Straight was hungry again and asked Crooked for bread.

"I'll give you some, if you let me take your right eye."

"Have pity, brother! Why, I would be blind."

"What of it? You can comfort yourself by knowing that you are honest and I am not."

Straight was faint with hunger, and so he agreed. "Very well," he said, "take my other eye, if you have no conscience."

Crooked blinded him, gave him a small piece of bread, and left him in the middle of the road. "I can't be bothered with leading you," he said.

The blind man ate the bread and struggled along as best he could, hoping to get to some village. But after a time he completely

lost his bearings and did not know in which direction to move. He
began praying ardently: "Lord, forsake me not, a sinner!" He
prayed and prayed, and presently he heard a mysterious voice saying to him:

"Turn to the right, and you will come to a gurgling spring in the forest; wash your eyes with the water from it and God will restore your sight. You will see a tall oak tree there; climb to the top and wait for the night."

The blind man did as he was told, and as soon as he had washed his eyes in the spring water, he regained his sight. Looking round he noticed a huge oak tree; the grass under it was all trampled down. He climbed to a top branch and waited for the night. As soon as it was dark, evil spirits came from all sides, settled down under the tree and began boasting of the wicked things they had done during the day. One said: "I've been to the beautiful princess again. I have tormented her for the last ten years! They are trying their best to drive me away from the palace, but I am too strong for them. Only the man who procures from a certain rich merchant his icon of the Mother of God can cure the princess."

In the morning when all the devils had gone, Straight climbed down from the tree and went in search of the rich merchant. He found him eventually and asked to be hired as a laborer. "I will serve you a whole year without any wages," he said, "only give me your icon of Our Lady."

The merchant agreed, and the good peasant served him a whole year, working hard and not sparing himself. When the year was up, he asked for the icon, and the merchant said: "I am very pleased with your work, but I do not wish to part with the icon; take money instead."

"No, I don't want your money; give me what we agreed upon."

"Oh, indeed! Serve me another year and then I'll give you the icon."

Well, there was nothing else to do, so Straight stayed for another year. But when the time for settlement came, the merchant was again loath to part with the icon. "I would rather pay you in money," he said, "but if you are bent on having the icon, work one more year for me."

It's little use arguing with the rich and the powerful; willy-nilly, Straight had to stay for a third year. He worked harder than ever and when his time was up, the merchant took the holy icon down from the wall and gave it to him. "Take it in God's name and go in peace, good man," he said.

Straight wrapped up the icon in a clean cloth and set off for the kingdom where the evil spirit tormented the beautiful princess. It was a long way to go, but he reached it at last and when he came to the city where she lived, he said that he could cure the princess. He was taken to the palace, and the king and queen led him to their daughter's chamber. The peasant asked for a bowl of water, plunged the icon of Our Lady three times into it, and told the princess to wash her face with the water. As soon as she had done so, evil spirits came out of her like a ball-shaped cloud of smoke and she recovered instantly. No trace of illness remained and she was as rosy, merry, and well as could be. Her parents were overjoyed and the king offered the good peasant money, jewels, and every kind of reward, but he would not take anything for what he had done. Then the princess said, "I will marry him." Her father agreed, and she and Straight were married that very day. A great feast was held in their honor, and Straight settled in the palace and was a son to the king.

After a time, he asked the king and queen to let him go home to see his old mother. The princess said, "Let us go together." So they set off, the two of them, in a royal coach drawn by splendid horses. They drove on and on, and one day they saw Crooked walking along. The king's son-in-law ordered the coachman to stop and called out, "Hello, brother! don't you know me? Do you remember how you argued with me that it was better to live by crooked means than by straight, and how you put out my eyes?"

Crooked was frightened and did not know what to do.

"Don't be afraid; I am not angry with you," said Straight, and he told Crooked all that had happened to him: how he regained his sight, and worked for the rich merchant, and married the beautiful princess.

Crooked heard his story and determined to go to the gurgling spring in the forest. "Perhaps I'll also hear something to my advantage," he thought.

He went to the forest, found the gurgling brook, climbed up the oak tree, and waited for the night to come. At the stroke of midnight evil spirits gathered under the oak; they saw Crooked, pulled him down, and tore him to pieces.

Prince Daniel

A certain princess had two beautiful children, a boy called Daniel, and a girl. She loved them dearly and was very proud of them. One day an old witch came to visit her; she complimented the princess on her children, was extremely amiable and, on leaving, presented her with a ring.

"If you want your son to be happy and prosperous, let him always wear this ring and marry a girl whom it will fit," said the witch.

The mother was very pleased with the present and put the ring on her son's finger as soon as he came of age. On her deathbed she charged him to marry a girl whom the ring would fit. He promised to do her bidding and set about looking for a wife. There were many eligible girls, but every time that he chose one, the ring was either too big or too small for her. At first he sought a wife among girls of noble rank, but was finally reduced to trying the ring on every girl he met—and all to no purpose. He came home one day quite dejected and said to his sister:

"I've been all over our princedom and can't find one girl whom the ring fits! It seems I shall have to remain single all my life."

"What a peculiar ring!" said his sister. "Let me have a look at it."

She put it on her finger and the ring seemed to cling to it and shine more brightly, as though it had been made for her.

"Why, sister, it's you who are destined to be my bride! I'll marry you."

"What folly is this, brother? It's against God's law to marry a sister. You are joking!"

"No, I am not. I'll marry you this very day. Make haste and get ready."

His sister pleaded with him and tried to shame him, but it was no use—he was determined to take her for his wife.

The poor princess sat down in the porch and wept bitterly. Three pilgrim women walked past, and though she was distraught with grief, she invited them to come in, and she set food and drink before them. They saw that she had been weeping and asked the reason. When she had told them her story, they said: "Don't you worry. Make four dolls and put one in each corner of your room. When your brother calls you to go to church, say that you are coming, but sit still."

She thanked the pilgrim women, made the dolls, and put them in the four corners of her room. Meanwhile her brother had dressed for the wedding and called her. She answered, "I shan't be long, brother; I am just fastening my shoe." And the dolls sang, spinning around and around:

> *Hide and seek, but all in vain,*
> *Hide and never be found again.*
> *Brother would his sister marry,*
> *Under the ground she must tarry.*
> *Good earth, give way!*
> *Sister, speed away!*

The ground began to give way under the maiden's feet and she sank into it up to her waist. Her brother called again: "Come—it's time we were in church.

"In a minute; I am just tying my sash."

The dolls went on singing. Now only the princess' head could be seen. Prince Daniel called for the third time: "Come along!"

"Coming. I've only my earrings to put on." The dolls went on singing, and his sister sank through the ground.

Prince Daniel called louder and louder, but she did not come. He grew angry and burst open the door. His sister was not in the room, and the dolls in the corners kept repeating:

> *Good earth, give way!*
> *Sister, speed away!*

He seized an ax, chopped the dolls to pieces, and threw them into the fire.

The princess meanwhile found herself in the underworld. She walked on and on and presently came upon a hut on hen's feet; the hut did not stand still but kept turning around. "Little hut, little hut, turn your back to the forest and your front to me," she said; the hut stopped and the door opened. In the room a beautiful girl sat embroidering a piece of silk with gold and silver. She met her guest kindly and said with a sigh: "Dear friend, why did you come? I live here with the ogress Baba Yagá;* she is out just now, but when she comes back it will go ill with you."

The princess was greatly alarmed, but since there was no way out, the two girls sat down to the embroidery together. They worked and talked, and after a time they heard Baba Yagá coming. The hostess quickly changed her guest into a needle and stuck the needle into a broom that stood by the door. No sooner had she done it than the ogress walked in.

"Fe-fi-fo-fum! I believe I smell a Russian!" she cried.

"It's no wonder," the maiden answered, "some passers-by came in for a drink of water."

---

* A Baba Yagá is a special kind of witch; she is always an ugly old woman and sometimes an ogress.

"Why did you let them go?"

"They were old, Granny; too tough for you."

"Mind you bring in everyone who comes and let no one out!" said the ogress and then she went off hunting.

When she had gone, the two girls sat down to the embroidery again and talked happily. But presently they heard Baba Yagá again and once more the guest had to be changed into a needle. The witch came in, sniffed the air and said, "I believe there's a Russian smell in the room!"

"Yes, Granny. Two old men came in just now to warm themselves, but they wouldn't stay, much as I asked them."

The ogress was hungry, so after some grumbling she set out hunting again.

The girls went back to their embroidery and as they worked they spoke of how they could run away from the wicked witch. They had not talked long when the ogress suddenly appeared in the doorway. "Fe-fi-fo-fum! Surely I smell a Russian?" she said with a leer.

"Yes, Granny. Here is a princess waiting for you."

The princess looked at Baba Yagá and nearly fainted with horror! She was a hideous old woman with sharp protruding teeth and a nose that almost reached to the ceiling.

"Now then, don't sit there with your arms folded!" she shouted. "Bring in some logs and heat the stove."

The girls brought in a lot of oak and maple logs and heated the stove till it was red hot. The witch took a broad spade and told the princess to sit down on it. She obeyed, but when Baba Yagá tried to push her into the oven, she stuck out one leg so that she could not be pushed in.

"You silly girl; you don't know how to sit properly!" cried the witch. "You must keep still."

The princess sat down properly, but when Baba Yagá tried to put her into the oven, she stuck out her other leg.

The witch was furious and pulled her back. "None of your

pranks, my beauty! Sit still, like this: look at me!" And she flopped herself down onto the spade, stretching out her legs in front of her.

The girls at once pushed her into the oven, shut the oven door, plastered it with clay, blocked it with heavy logs, and ran away, taking with them the embroidered cloth, a brush, and a comb.

They had run some distance when they heard someone whistling behind them. They looked round and saw to their dismay that the witch had scrambled out of the oven and was now overtaking them.

"Ha-ha!" she cried, "You shan't escape me now!"

What were they to do? They threw the brush behind them, and an enormous stretch of tall reeds grew up all at once; the stems were so close together that a snake could not have crawled between them.

The witch spread out her claws, cleared a path, and was after them again. This time they threw the comb in her way, and a big forest sprang up where it fell; the trees were so close together and the undergrowth so thick that a bird could not have flown though it.

Baba Yagá sharpened her teeth, and bit into tree after tree, up-rooting and hurling them aside. In this way she cleared a path, and although the girls meanwhile had run a fair distance, she was soon on their track again. They ran faster and faster till their breath failed them . . . and the witch was close on their heels. In despair they flung behind them the gold-embroidered cloth, and a wide, deep river of fire flowed between them and the witch. She rose up into the air intending to fly across, but fell into the flames and was burned to ashes.

The two girls were safe from her now, but they were homeless and did not know where to go; they sat down to rest in a garden that lay on their way. As it happened it was Prince Daniel's garden, but his sister did not recognize it. The prince's servant saw them and ran to his master in great excitement. "There are two beautiful ladies in your garden," he said, "and they are exactly alike so that

there is no telling one from the other. I believe one of them is your sister, but I do not know which."

Prince Daniel came out into the garden and spoke to them, but he could not say which of the two was his sister and she would not reveal herself. What was he to do?

"I'll tell you what," said his servant, "take a pig's bladder, fill it with red wine, and hide it under your arm. I'll pretend to be a brigand and stick a knife into it: the wine will flow, and your sister will think it is blood and declare herself."

They carried out the plan. The servant rushed at the prince and stuck a knife into his side; blood gushed out, the prince fell, and his sister flew to his aid. She wept and called him her darling brother, and kissed him. Then he jumped up and threw his arms around her, beside himself with joy. He found an excellent husband for her that very day, and himself married her companion, whom the ring fitted to perfection; and they all lived happily for the rest of their lives.

A Lucky Child

There once lived a rich merchant and his wife; they had plenty of gold and silver and of every kind of goods, but they had no children. They prayed and prayed that God would give them a child. They gave food and drink to the poor, and distributed many alms, and at last decided to build a long bridge over an impassable bog for the benefit of all Christian people. The merchant spent a great deal of money building it, and when the work was finished he sent for his bailiff, Fyodor, and said to him:

"Go and sit by the bridge and listen to what people say about me. I wonder if they will thank me or find fault?"

Fyodor went and listened. Three holy men walked over the bridge and said one to another: "How shall we reward the man who built this bridge? Let him have a lucky son! Whatever that child wishes, it shall come to pass; whatever he asks of God, it shall be given him."

The bailiff heard all this and went home. "Well, Fyodor, what do people say?" his master asked him.

"Oh, different things. Some say you've done a good deed, and others think you built the bridge simply out of pride and vainglory."

That same year the merchant's wife gave birth to a son; he was christened and laid in a cradle. The bailiff envied the parents' good fortune and, in the dead of night, when everyone was fast asleep, he killed a pigeon and smeared the mother's lips and hands and the bed with its blood; then he stole the child and sent it away to be brought up by a foster mother.

The parents were distressed to find that the baby had disappeared and could not think what had become of it. They questioned all their household, and the wicked bailiff pointed to the mother and said: "Look, her hands and mouth are covered with blood, she has eaten the baby!"

The merchant believed him and had his wife put in prison. After a few years Fyodor left his master and went to live by the sea, taking the little boy with him. When he wanted anything he just said to the boy "Wish this and that"—and the wish was fulfilled. One day he said: "I'll tell you what, my boy! Ask God that there should be a new city here, and that a crystal bridge should stretch across the sea right to the king's palace, and that his daughter should marry me."

The boy did as he was told, and at once a crystal bridge stretched across the sea, and a beautiful city with splendid palaces and churches appeared on the shore. The following morning the king beyond the sea looked out of the window and was surprised to see the crystal bridge and the fine city at the other end of it. "Who could have built such a marvellous bridge?" he asked. When he heard that it was Fyodor, he said: "If he is so clever, I'll give him my daughter for wife."

It did not take long to arrange the marriage, and Fyodor soon began to rule over the new city. He kept the boy as his servant and treated him very badly. The poor child received plenty of blows and abuse, and very little food.

One evening Fyodor was lying comfortably on the couch with his wife beside him, and the boy sat huddled in a dark corner weeping bitterly. The princess asked her husband:

"Tell me, how have you come by all your wealth? You were only a bailiff to begin with."

"All my wealth and power come from the boy whom I stole from his parents."

"How was that?"

"I was bailiff to a rich merchant, and it was promised that he should have a lucky son whose every wish would come true. When the baby was born, I stole it, and to cover up my tracks I slandered the mother, saying that she had eaten her son."

The boy overheard all this; he came out of his corner and said: "At my petition and by God's decree, turn into a dog, you scoundrel!"

Instantly Fyodor became a dog. The boy put an iron chain on its neck and went to find his father. When they came to the house, he said to the merchant: "Please, good man, give me some burning coals."

"What for?"

"To feed my dog."

"What are you talking about!" the merchant said. "Who ever has seen a dog eat live coals?"

"And who ever has seen a mother eat her own child?" answered the boy. "You must know the truth, Father: I am your son, and this dog is your old bailiff, Fyodor, who stole me and slandered my mother."

The merchant asked how it had all happened, and hastened to let his wife out of prison. Afterwards they all went to live in the new city that had risen by the sea at the boy's request. The princess went back to her father, and Fyodor remained a vile dog till he died.

Bird Language

There once lived in a town on the river Volga a merchant with his wife and his son Vassili, a good little boy, intelligent beyond his years.

One day when they were all sitting at dinner, the nightingale in a cage on the wall broke into such a beautiful song that the father said: "I wish I knew what the bird is singing about! It's as though it meant something by its song."

"I know what its song means," said the little boy, "but I am afraid to tell you."

"Don't be afraid, tell us!" the parents insisted. So at last Vassili said with tears:

"The nightingale says that a time will come when you will both wait upon me like servants: my father will bring water for me to wash my hands, and my mother will hold the towel."

The merchant and his wife were so put out by this that they decided to get rid of their son. When night came, they took the sleeping boy in his cot down to the river, placed him in a boat, and pushed it off. As they did so, they noticed that the nightingale perched on the child's pillow.

The boat floated downstream, and presently a ship overtook it. The men on board saw the sleeping child and took pity on him. They picked him up, and the nightingale followed. Everyone liked the boy, and the captain promised to bring him up as his own son.

A day or two later, Vassili said to the captain: "The nightingale warns us that a bad storm is blowing up so that we had better take shelter by the bank." The captain took no heed of his words, but soon a terrible storm burst upon them, broke down one of the masts, tore up the sails, and very nearly sank the ship.

When they had done the necessary repairs and set sail again, Vassili warned the captain once more: "The nightingale tells me that twelve pirate ships are sailing toward us; we had better get out of their way."

This time the captain heeded the warning and took his ship to a narrow strait between two islets near the shore, and from their hiding place they saw twelve pirate ships sail past.

After that the captain had every confidence in Vassili, and the boy saved him and his men from many a danger both on land and water. He could understand what birds said and they always gave him good advice.

One day their ship landed at the royal city of Hvalynsk.* The king who reigned there had for many years been greatly troubled by three ravens that flew day and night in front of the palace disturbing him with their loud cries. Every device had been used to drive them away, but all to no purpose. At last the king issued a proclamation and had it put up in harbors and at crossroads and in market places. It said: "The man who succeeds in driving away the ravens from the palace windows shall be given half the kingdom and the youngest of the king's daughters for a wife; but if he undertakes the job and does not succeed, he will be beheaded."

---

* The old name for the Caspian sea is "Hvalynsky Sea" and possibly "the royal city of Hvalynsk" refers to Astrahan which, up to 1556, when it was captured by the Russians, had been the capital of a Tatar Khanate.

Many people were tempted by the hope of marrying the king's daughter, but they all had to lay their heads under the ax.

When Vassili had read the proclamation, he begged the captain to let him go to the king and drive away the ravens. The captain did his best to dissuade him but had to give in at last. "Very well, go," he said, "but if you come to grief, it will be your own fault."

Vassili went to the palace, told the king why he had come, and asked to open the window around which the ravens were flying. He listened to their cries and said to the king: "Your Majesty, as you see there are three of them: the raven, his wife, and their young son. The parents cannot agree to whom the son should belong, and ask you to decide for them. Tell them, Your Majesty, to whom does the son belong?"

"To the father," answered the king, and as soon as he said the words, the raven and his son flew away in one direction, and the mother raven in another.

After this, the king took Vassili to live with him and treated him as a son; the boy grew up into a fine young man, married the princess, and took half the kingdom as her dowry.

One day he thought he would like to see other countries, and set out to travel. He stopped for the night in a certain town and in the morning asked for water to wash in. His host brought in the water, and the hostess held the towel ready. Vassili talked with them and discovered that they were his father and mother; he wept for joy and fell at their feet. Afterwards he took them with him to his kingdom and they all lived together happily.

The Frog-Princess

Once upon a time there lived a king who had three sons. When they came of age, he said to them: "My dear sons, it is time you married, and this is how I would have you choose your wives. Take your bows and arrows, go outside the city walls, and each shoot an arrow. Wherever your arrow falls, there will be your bride."

The three princes did as their father bade them and each shot an arrow. The eldest's arrow fell by a nobleman's mansion, and he took the nobleman's daughter for wife. The second son's arrow fell by a merchant's house, and he took the merchant's daughter for wife. The third son, Ivan Tsarevitch, shot his arrow so far that he had to walk all day in search of it, and when at last he found it, it was in a marsh, and a frog held it in its mouth. The frog said, "Take me home with you, Ivan Tsarevitch." So he put it in his pocket and brought it home.

When he had told his story to his father, the king said, "Well, it evidently is your fate to marry the frog—there is no alternative." Ivan Tsarevitch was very sad, but he would not disobey his father, and the three weddings were celebrated on the same day.

After a while, the king called his three sons and said to them:

"My dear sons, I want to know what your wives can do. Bid each of them bake a loaf of bread for me by tomorrow."

The two elder sons were not in the least put out by this request, for they knew that their wives could bake, put poor Ivan Tsarevitch came home looking so dejected that the frog asked him:

"What ails you, Ivan Tsarevitch? Why do you hang your head? Has your father said some unkind word to you?"

"I might well be sad," said he. "My father has bidden each of his daughters-in-law to bake him a loaf by tomorrow, and you cannot do it."

"Is that all? Don't you trouble, Ivan Tsarevitch. Have your supper, say your prayers, and go to bed: morning is wiser than evening."

Ivan Tsarevitch took her advice, and as soon as he had fallen asleep, the frog came out on to the front steps, threw off her frog's skin, and became a beautiful princess—Vassilissa the Wise. She clapped her hands and called out in a loud voice:

"My faithful servants! Bring me by the morning a loaf of bread such as I used to eat in my father's palace!"

When Ivan Tsarevitch woke up, he found by his bedside a fine wheaten loaf decorated with designs in sugar. He wrapped it up in a white cloth and carried it merrily to his father the king.

The two elder brothers had already brought their loaves to the palace. The nobleman's daughter was not so good at baking as the merchant's, and her bread was a little heavy, but it looked well enough. The brothers were confident that the king would praise their wives' skill, and joked about Ivan Tsarevitch: "I expect his frog will send a little mud pie," they said; "that's about all she can contrive to do."

Ivan Tsarevitch came in just as his father entered the room from another door, and his brothers had not had time to see what he brought. But when all the loaves were put before the king, everyone was amazed at the wonderful loaf presented by Ivan Tsarevitch. The king was so delighted with it that he ate half of it right away, after merely tasting the two other loaves. He asked Ivan Tsarevitch to thank his frog-wife and said many flattering things about her cookery.

So the first trial ended well for Ivan Tsarevitch. After a few days, the king demanded that each of his daughters-in-law should make him a carpet by the following morning, for he wanted to see how well they could weave. Again poor Ivan Tsarevitch came home greatly troubled.

"What ails you, Ivan Tsarevitch? Why do you hang your head? Has your father said some unkind word to you?" asked the frog.

"I might well be sad!" he answered. "My father wants each of his daughters-in-law to make him a carpet by tomorrow—and how can you do that?"

"Don't you trouble, Ivan Tsarevitch," answered the frog. "Have your supper, say your prayers, and go to bed: morning is wiser than evening."

Ivan Tsarevitch did as he was told, and as soon as he had fallen asleep, the frog came out on to the front steps, threw off her frog's skin, and became the beautiful Princess Vassilissa. She clapped her hands and called out in a loud voice:

"My faithful servants! Bring me by tomorrow the carpet I used to sit on in my father's palace."

When Ivan Tsarevitch woke up in the morning, he saw spread out before him a wonderful carpet all ablaze with color: there were embroidered on it all the rivers and cities, forests and mountains of his father's kingdom, so that one could see it all at a glance. Overjoyed, he rolled up the carpet, wrapped it in a linen cloth, and almost ran to the palace.

The two elder brothers were already there, showing to each other their wives' handiwork. The nobleman's daughter was better than the merchant's at weaving and embroidering, but both carpets were quite presentable. The brothers thought that the frog could not make a carpet at all, so they were sure they would score over Ivan Tsarevitch. But when he came and unfolded his carpet, the king was so enchanted with it that he would not even look at the other two. He ordered the frog's carpet to be hung up on the wall of his throne room, for he said it was much too good to put on the floor.

So the second trial went off successfully for Ivan Tsarevitch.

When a few days had passed, the king again called his sons together and said to them:

"My dear sons, I know which of your wives is the most skillful; I now want to know which is the most beautiful of the three. Bring them to dinner with me tomorrow."

This time Ivan Tsarevitch came home feeling so miserable that he did not even wait for his wife to ask what ailed him. He told her of his own accord what the trouble was. And she said again: "Don't you trouble, Ivan Tsarevitch. Have your supper, say your prayers, and go to bed. In the morning go to the palace alone, and when you hear rumbling and rattling, say 'It's my frog coming in her little box.'"

Ivan Tsarevitch followed her advice, and when next morning he arrived at the palace alone, his brothers were already there with their wives, decked out in their best. They asked jokingly if he had brought the frog in his pocket, but he replied that she would come by herself later on.

Presently, a loud rumbling and rattling were heard. All rushed to the windows to see what it was, but Ivan Tsarevitch said calmly, "Oh, it's my frog, coming in her little box." As he said it, a splendid golden carriage drew up at the palace doors and a beautiful princess stepped out. He ran to meet her and introduced her to the king and to the rest of the family as his wife, the frog.

The king was enchanted with her beauty and grace; he made her sit on his right at the table and Ivan Tsarevitch on his left. Her conversation was so engaging that both he and his three sons gave their whole attention to her, while her sisters-in-law watched her enviously, deciding to imitate everything she did. They noticed that after picking the bones of the roast swan, she put the bones in her left sleeve; after drinking wine, she poured the last few drops out of the goblet into her right sleeve; so they did the same.

When dinner was over, the king led the Frog-Princess on to the terrace to show her the view; standing beside him, she suddenly waved her right arm, and behold, a lovely lake appeared in front of the palace; she waved her left arm, and a flock of beautiful white swans alighted on the blue waters. The king was delighted and was complimenting her on her accomplishments, when her sisters-in-law, thinking they could do the same, also waved their arms. But their wet sleeves flapped against the king's face, and the swan's bones fell rattling all over the terrace. The king was very angry and ordered them both out of the palace.

Ivan Tsarevitch was overjoyed to find that his wife was a lovely princess, but fearing that she might turn into a frog again, he hurried home, found the frog's skin, and burned it in the fire. When she returned from the palace and found that the skin was gone, she cried out in horror: "Oh, what have you done, Ivan Tsarevitch! Had you waited a little longer, I would have been yours forever, but now we must part. You must look for me over the hills and far away, and it may be years and years before you find me." With these words, she turned into a swan and flew out of the window.

Ivan Tsarevitch wept bitterly, and after saying good-by to his father, set out in search of her.

He wandered far and wide, over forests and dales, but could find no trace of her. One day when he had almost given up hope, he met an old man who asked him where he was going. Ivan Tsarevitch told him of his trouble. The old man shook his head and said:

"You did wrong in burning the frog's skin. You did not clothe her with it, and you had no business to destroy it. It was your wife's father who bewitched her: he was angry because she proved to be cleverer than he and so he turned her into a frog for a space of three years. It won't be easy for you to find her, but here is a ball which will show you the way."

And he gave the prince a ball of thread. Ivan Tsarevitch thanked him and followed the ball, which took him through a thick forest to which there seemed no end. He walked on and on and at last in the gathering dusk saw a glimmer of light before him. The light came from the window of a little hut that had hen's feet and kept turning around and around. Ivan Tsarevitch said to it: "Little hut, little hut, turn your back to the forest and your front to me!"

The hut turned, and he went in. A grim old woman bent almost double with age sat by the stove; her nose nearly met her chin, and a long yellow tooth stuck out of her mouth. Seeing Ivan Tsarevitch, she called out in a shrill voice:

"That's a wonder! No Russian man has ever been seen or heard of in these parts, and here is one in the flesh! What have you come for?"

"That's not the way to greet a guest, Granny," Ivan Tsarevitch replied. "You should first heat the bathhouse and let me have a good wash, and then give me supper and make up a bed for me, and in the morning you may ask questions."

The old Baba Yagá did as he wished, and after he had had a good night's rest, he told her his story.

"I cannot help you," she said, "for I know not where your wife is. But go to my elder sister—she is wiser than I am and knows more."

So Ivan Tsarevitch thanked her and went off to find her elder sister. The ball of thread rolled before him showing him the way. After a long day's journey, he came to another hut on hen's feet that kept turning around and around.

"Little hut, little hut! Turn your back to the forest and your front to me," he said, and the hut obeyed.

The old woman who lived in the hut looked less ancient than her younger sister, and learning that Ivan Tsarevitch had come from her, received him kindly. She heated the bathhouse for him, gave him supper, and made up a good soft bed for him to sleep in, and in the morning she asked what his trouble was. When he had told her, she said:

"Princess Vassilissa is living with my eldest sister and I will tell you how to rescue her. By day my sister turns her into a spindle and spins gold on it. You must take the spindle, break it into two, and throw the sharp end behind you and the blunt one in front of you. Then the spell will be broken."

Ivan Tsarevitch thanked the old witch with all his heart and set off to find the eldest sister. The ball rolled along merrily leading him through the depths of the endless forest, but it took him days and days to reach his destination. Before going into the witch's hut, he peeped in at the window and saw a big, fierce-looking woman, by far the most vigorous of the three sisters, spinning golden thread. When she had finished, she put the spindle and the gold she had spun into a casket, and locked it up. But Ivan Tsarevitch saw where she put the key, and as soon as she went out of the hut, he rushed in, opened the casket, took out the spindle, and broke it into two, throwing the sharp end behind him and the blunt end in front of himself. Instantly there stood before him his dear wife, Princess Vassilissa the Wise. She threw herself into his arms and thanked him for delivering her from the evil spell. She called for a magic carpet and they flew home straight away. The old king was delighted to see them, and made Ivan Tsarevitch heir to the throne.

Marya Morévna

Ivan Tsarevitch had three lovely sisters: Olga-Tsarevna, Marfa-Tsarevna, and Anna-Tsarevna. His parents had charged him on their deathbed to let his sisters marry the first suitors that presented themselves. "Don't keep them at home too long," his father and mother said.

One fine summer day, Ivan Tsarevitch went for a walk with his sisters. All of a sudden, dark storm clouds gathered in the sky and covered the sun. "Let's go home, dear sisters," he said. No sooner had they returned to the palace than there was a terrible thunderclap, the ceiling was riven in two, and a bright-colored falcon flew in. It threw itself on the floor and became a handsome young man.

"Greetings, Ivan Tsarevitch!" he said. "I've been here before as a guest, and now I come as a suitor. Will you give me your sister Olga-Tsarevna in marriage?"

"If she is willing, I shall not hold her back—let her be married in God's name."

Princess Olga consented, the falcon married her, and bore her off to his kingdom.

One day followed another, weeks and months flew by, and soon a year had passed. Ivan Tsarevitch was once more in the garden with his sisters. Again a storm cloud blew up blotting out the sun. "Let's go indoors, dear sisters," he said, and as soon as they had gone in, there came a peal of thunder, the ceiling was riven in two, and an eagle flew into the room. It flung itself against the floor and became a handsome young man.

"Greetings, Ivan Tsarevitch!" he said. "I have been here before as a guest and now I come as a suitor. Will you give me your sister Marfa-Tsarevna in marriage?"

"If she is willing, I shall not hold her back—let her be your wife." Marfa-Tsarevna agreed, and so the eagle married her and bore her away to his kingdom.

Another year passed. One day Ivan Tsarevitch and his youngest sister were out together in the bright sunshine. Suddenly black clouds came up; there was a rush of wind and a distant rumble of thunder. "Let's hurry home, dear sister," he said. Just as they came into the hall, there was a flash of lightning, a clap of thunder, the ceiling was riven in two, and a raven flew in. It dashed itself against the floor and became a handsome young man. The falcon and the eagle were handsome, too, but this one was the best looking of all.

"Greetings, Ivan Tsarevitch!" he said. "I've been here as a guest before, and now I come as a suitor. Will you give me your sister Anna-Tsarevna in marriage?"

"She is free to decide for herself; if she is willing, I shall not hinder her." Anna-Tsarevna married the raven, and he carried her off to his kingdom.

Ivan Tsarevitch was left alone. He lived for a whole year without his sisters and felt very lonely. "I'll go and see them," he decided. He made ready for the journey and set off. He rode on and on, and one day he saw a battlefield covered with dead and wounded men. "Is there a man alive?" he asked. "If there is, tell me who defeated this host?"

A man answered and said: "It was the young queen, Marya Morévna the Beautiful."

Ivan Tsarevitch journeyed on and presently came upon an encampment of white tents in a green meadow. The young queen, Marya Morévna the Beautiful, came forward to meet him. "Greetings, Tsarevitch!" she said. "Where are you going, and is it of your own will or by compulsion?"

"Young warriors go as they please," he answered.

"Well, if you are in no hurry, stay in my tents for a time." Ivan Tsarevitch was glad to do so and spent two nights in the camp. Marya Morévna fell in love with him and he married her.

They went back to her kingdom and lived there happily. After a time the young queen made ready to go to war; she left Ivan Tsarevitch in charge of everything at home and said to him: "Go wherever you like and do what you please, but on no account look into this closet."

This was too much to ask: no sooner had Marya Morévna gone, than Ivan Tsarevitch rushed to the forbidden closet and peeped in. In the closet was Old Bones the Deathless hung up by twelve iron chains.

Old Bones the Deathless begged Ivan Tsarevitch: "Have pity on me; give me a drink! I've been languishing here for ten years without food or drink, and my throat is parched."

The Tsarevitch gave him a pail of water; the old wizard drank it up and asked for more. "One pail is not enough to slake my thirst, give me another."

The Tsarevitch gave him another pailful. Old Bones drank it and asked for more. When he had drunk a third pailful, he regained his strength, shook the chains, and broke all the twelve at once. "Thank you, Ivan Tsarevitch!" said he. "Now you shall never see Marya Morévna again." He flew in a whirlwind out of the window, overtook the young queen Marya Morévna the Beautiful, and carried her off.

Ivan Tsarevitch wept bitterly and set out in search of his wife. "Whatever befalls me, I will find her," he decided. He walked for two whole days, and on the morning of the third came to a beautiful palace; an oak was growing in front of it, and on the oak sat a bright-colored falcon. It flew down, flung itself against the ground, became a handsome young man, and cried out: "Why, it's my dear brother-in-law! How are you?"

Olga-Tsarevna ran out, beside herself with joy. She fell on Ivan Tsarevitch's neck, asked him how he was, and told him all her news. He spent three days with her and the falcon, and then said: "I cannot stay longer with you, for I must go and seek my wife, Marya Morévna."

"It won't be easy to find her," said the falcon. "Leave your silver spoon with us—we'll think of you when we look at it."

So he left his silver spoon with them, said good-by, and continued his journey.

He walked for two days and on the third day, at dawn, he came to another palace, even finer than the first. There was an oak tree in front of it, and an eagle sat on the tree. When the eagle saw Ivan Tsarevitch, it flung itself against the ground and became a handsome young man. "Make haste and get up, Marfa-Tsarevna," he cried; "here comes our dear brother!"

Marfa-Tsarevna ran out and embraced Ivan Tsarevitch joyfully, asked how he was, and told him all her news. Ivan Tsarevitch spent three days with her and her husband and then said he must continue his search for Marya Morévna.

"It won't be easy to find her," said the eagle. "Leave with us your silver fork—we'll look at it and think of you."

He left his silver fork with them, kissed them good-by, and went on his way.

He walked for two whole days and on the morning of the third came to a palace that was even more beautiful than the first two. An oak tree grew in front of it, and on the oak sat a raven. When the raven saw Ivan Tsarevitch, it flew down, hit the ground, and became a handsome young man. "Come quick, Anna-Tsarevna!" he cried. "Our dear brother is here."

Anna-Tsarevna, delighted, rushed out to meet her brother and could not make enough of him. She asked for his news and told him all about herself.

He spent three days with her and the raven and then said: "Good-by, I must go on looking for my wife, Marya Morévna, the beautiful queen."

"You will find it very difficult to rescue her," said the raven. "Leave your silver snuffbox with us—we'll think of you as we look at it."

Ivan Tsarevitch left the snuffbox with them, kissed them, and walked on.

He journeyed for two days and on the third he reached the place where Marya Morévna lived. She saw him from afar, ran out to meet him, and fell on his neck, weeping. "Oh, Ivan Tsarevitch," she cried, "why did you disobey me and look into the closet where Old Bones the Deathless was?"

"Forgive me," he answered. "Don't recall the past. Let's make haste and escape while Old Bones the Deathless is out of the way. Maybe he won't catch us."

So they made ready and rode away.

Old Bones the Deathless was out hunting; toward evening he turned home, but his horse kept stumbling. "Why do you stumble, you wretched nag?" he asked. "Do you scent trouble?"

"Ivan Tsarevitch has carried off Marya Morévna," the horse answered.

"Can we overtake them?"

"If we sow a field of wheat, and wait for it to ripen, and harvest it, and mill the grain into flour, and bake five ovenfuls of bread and eat it—we shall still have plenty of time to catch them."

Old Bones the Deathless galloped after Ivan Tsarevitch and overtook him. "I'll forgive you this time," he said, "because you've been kind and given me water to drink; and I'll forgive you a second time, but beware! If I catch you a third time, I'll chop you to pieces." He snatched Marya Morévna from him and carried her off.

Ivan Tsarevitch sat down on a stone and wept; then he went

back to Marya Morévna. Old Bones the Deathless happened to be out.

"Let's run away, Marya Morévna."

"Oh, Ivan Tsarevitch, he'll catch us!"

"Well, let him! Anyway we shall have spent a couple of hours together." So they made ready and rode off.

As Old Bones the Deathless was coming home, his horse stumbled under him. "Why do you stumble, you wretched nag?" he asked. "Do you scent trouble ahead?"

"Ivan Tsarevitch came and carried off Marya Morévna," the horse answered.

"Can we overtake them?"

"If you sow a field of barley, wait for it to ripen, harvest and thresh it, and then brew beer, drink it, and have a good sleep—there will still be time to catch them."

Old Bones set off at a gallop, overtook Ivan Tsarevitch, and said: "I told you, you shall never have Marya Morévna again," and he carried her off.

Ivan Tsarevitch wept, but after a time he dried his tears and went back to his wife. By a lucky chance Old Bones was not at home. "Let's escape, Marya Morévna," Ivan said.

"But, Ivan Tsarevitch, he'll overtake us and hack you to pieces."

"Well, let him! I cannot live without you." So they made ready and rode away.

In the evening, Old Bones was coming home and again his faithful horse stumbled under him. "Why do you stumble? Do you scent trouble ahead?"

"Ivan Tsarevitch came and took Marya Morévna with him."

Old Bones galloped after Ivan Tsarevitch, overtook him, hacked him to pieces, put the pieces into a barrel with iron bands around it, and threw it into the sea. Then he carried Marya Morévna back to his house again.

When this happened, the silver articles which Ivan Tsarevitch had left with his brothers-in-law grew tarnished. "Some misfortune must have happened to him," they said. The eagle flew to the sea, picked up the barrel, and brought it ashore; the raven flew to fetch some water of death; and the falcon brought some water of life. Then they all three met together, broke open the barrel, and took out the pieces of Ivan Tsarevitch's body. They washed them, placed them in proper order, and the raven sprinkled the water of death over them; the parts adhered together and the body became whole. Then the falcon sprinkled the water of life over it, and Ivan Tsarevitch moved, stretched his limbs, and stood up. "What a long sleep I've had," he said.

"You would have slept longer still if it had not been for us," said his brothers-in-law. "Come and stay with us now."

"No, brothers! I must go in search of Marya Morévna."

And once more he went to the house of Old Bones the Deathless. Marya Morévna saw him come; she rushed out to meet him and fell on his neck weeping for joy. "How did God raise you from the dead?" she asked. He told her all that had happened to him and begged her to find out how the old wizard had found his wonderful horse.

So Marya Morévna waited for an opportunity, and when Old Bones was in a good mood, began questioning him. He said to her: "East of the sun and west of the moon, beyond a river of fire, lives Baba Yagá; she has a mare on which she can ride all around the world in a single day, and a number of other fine mares. I served her as a herd for three days and did not let a single mare escape, and as a reward she gave me a foal."

"But how did you get across the river of fire?"

"Oh, I have a special kerchief—if I wave it three times to the right, it makes a fine bridge so high that the flames cannot reach it."

Marya Morévna repeated all this to Ivan Tsarevitch; then she secured the magic kerchief and gave it to him.

Ivan Tsarevitch set off to find Baba Yagá. He crossed the river of fire and walked on and on, without food or drink. Suddenly he saw a beautiful big bird with twelve chicks. "I'll kill one of those chicks for my dinner," he said aloud.

"Don't harm my chicks, Ivan Tsarevitch!" the bird begged. "One day I may be of use to you."

Ivan took pity on the bird and went on his way. Presently he came upon a nest of wild bees in the forest. I must take some honey, he thought; but the queen bee said: "Don't touch my honey, Ivan Tsarevitch; one day I may be able to help you."

He left the nest alone and walked on. After a time he came upon a lioness with a cub. I'll eat the lion cub, he thought. I am quite faint with hunger.

"Don't kill my cub, Ivan Tsarevitch!" the lioness pleaded. "One day I may be of service to you."

"Very well, I won't touch your cub," he said, and went on his way hungry.

He reached at last Baba Yagá's house. There were twelve posts around it, and all but one had human heads stuck on them.

"Good morning, Granny!"

"Good morning, Ivan Tsarevitch! Have you come of your own will or been sent here?"

"I've come to earn a warrior horse from you."

"By all means, Ivan Tsarevitch! I don't require a year's service, but only three days. If you herd my mares and don't lose one of them, I'll give you a warrior horse; but if not, your head will be stuck on that post over there." Ivan Tsarevitch agreed, and Baba Yagá gave him food and drink and told him to set to work.

No sooner had he driven the mares into the open than they rushed away and vanished from sight. In dismay, Ivan Tsarevitch sat down on a stone and wept; and then he dropped asleep. At sunset the beautiful bird of the forest flew up to him and cried, "Wake up, Ivan Tsarevitch! All the mares are at home." He got up, and as he walked back to Baba Yagá's house, he heard her scolding the mares. "Why did you come home?" she asked them.

"What else could we do? Flocks of birds from all over the world came and nearly plucked our eyes out."

"Well, tomorrow don't run about the meadows, but hide in the forest."

The next morning, Baba Yagá said, "Mind, Ivan Tsarevitch, if you lose a single one of my mares, your head shall be hoisted up on my fence!"

He took the mares into the meadows, but they made straight for the forest and were gone in a twinkling of an eye. Ivan Tsarevitch again sat down on a stone and wept till he dropped asleep. The sun went down behind the forest. The lioness ran up to him and said: "Get up, Ivan Tsarevitch! The mares are all safely in the stables." He walked to Baba Yagá's house and heard her shouting and swearing at her mares: "Why did you come back?" she asked them.

"But what were we do do? The forest was full of wild beasts that nearly tore us to pieces."

"Well, tomorrow you must go into the sea."

The following morning Baba Yagá again sent Ivan out with her mares and warned him: "If you lose a single one of them, you are done for."

As soon as Ivan Tsarevitch had taken the mares into the open country, they galloped off and made for the sea. There they went up to their necks into the water and would not stir, call them as he would. Seeing that he could do nothing with them, he sat down on a stone and wept; and presently he dropped asleep. When the sun had set, a bee settled on his shoulder and said: "Get up, Ivan Tsarevitch, the mares are all at home. When you go back to Baba Yagá, don't show yourself to her, but hide behind the feeding trough in the stables. You will find a mangy colt there, lying on rotten straw; take it and go out of the place in the dead of the night."

Ivan Tsarevitch got up, stole up to the stables, and hid behind the manger. Baba Yagá was shouting and scolding her mares. "Why did you come back?" she asked them.

"What were we to do?" said the mares. "Bees came from all over the world and began stinging us."

Baba Yagá went to sleep, and at midnight Ivan Tsarevitch stole the mangy colt, mounted it, and galloped to the river of fire. When he reached it, he waved his kerchief three times to the right, and a strong fine bridge appeared over the flames. He crossed to the other side and waved his kerchief to the left twice only, and the bridge became very slender and unsafe.

When Baba Yagá woke up in the morning, the mangy colt was nowhere to be seen. She rushed in pursuit, rattling away in her iron bowl, driving it along with a long sharp pole and sweeping her tracks with a broom. She came to the river of fire, saw the bridge, and thought, That's a fine bridge! But when she reached the middle, the bridge broke and the old witch fell into the river—and that was the end of her.

Ivan Tsarevitch reared his colt in green meadows and it grew into a splendid horse. Then he went to find Marya Morévna again. She ran out to meet him and fell on his neck, overjoyed. "Come away with me," he said.

"I am afraid, Ivan Tsarevitch! If Old Bones catches you, he'll hack you to pieces again."

"He won't catch us. I have a splendid horse now, swift as a bird." So they mounted his horse and went off.

Old Bones the Deathless was coming home and his horse stumbled under him. "Why do you stumble, you wretched nag?" he asked. "Do you scent trouble ahead?"

"Ivan Tsarevitch came and carried off Marya Morévna."

"Can we catch them?"

"There's no telling! Ivan Tsarevitch has a fine horse now."

"No, I won't stand this! I must go after them," said Old Bones. After a time he did overtake Ivan Tsarevitch, and jumping down to the ground, raised his sharp sword to smite him. But at that moment Ivan Tsarevitch's horse hit Old Bones the Deathless with its hoof and smashed his head in, and Ivan Tsarevitch finished him off with his battle-ax. Then the Tsarevitch built up a huge pile of logs, set them on fire, burned the old wizard's body, and scattered the ashes in the wind.

Marya Morévna mounted the horse that Old Bones had ridden, Ivan Tsarevitch rode his own, and they went to pay a visit, first to the raven, then to the eagle, and then to the falcon. Everywhere they were greeted joyfully and their hosts said: "Ah, Ivan Tsarevitch, we had scarcely hoped to see you again. Well, it isn't for nothing that you braved all those dangers—another such beauty as Marya Morévna could not be found in the whole wide world!"

After staying with their relatives, Ivan Tsarevitch and Marya Morévna returned to their own kingdom and lived happily all their days.

The Huntsman
and His Wife

There was once a huntsman whose business it was to provide game for the king's table. His cottage stood at the edge of a huge forest which stretched for miles and miles to the east of the city, and every morning he went there to hunt; there were plenty of wild birds and animals in the forest. One day, however, he spent hours looking for something to shoot and could find nothing. At last he saw a turtledove and took aim, thinking that at least he would not come home empty-handed. But all of a sudden the turtledove said to him, "Don't shoot me, hunter! Take me home and put me on the window sill; as soon as I go to sleep, strike me with your right hand, and that will bring you luck."

The huntsman was greatly astonished, for never in his life had he heard birds speak. He took the turtledove home, put it on the window sill, and watched. After a time it hid its head under its wing and went to sleep. The huntsman raised his right arm and struck the bird lightly—it fell to the ground, and in its place there stood a beautiful maiden.

"You knew how to capture me, and now you must learn how to keep me! You shall be my bridegroom, and I shall be your wife."

The huntsman was only too glad to marry her, and they were very happy together.

One summer's day, the king went hunting in the forest with several of his courtiers. They had no luck and were coming home tired, hot, and thirsty. When they saw a cottage at the forest edge, they knocked at the door to ask for a drink. It was the huntsman's cottage; his wife opened the door and brought out a pitcher of cold, crystal-clear water. The king could not take his eyes off her and thought he had never seen a more beautiful woman. By the time he arrived at the palace, he had fully made up his mind to get rid of her husband and to marry her himself.

He called for his chamberlain, who was a crafty old man, and asked his advice. The chamberlain pondered the matter and said, "The best thing would be to set the huntsman some task which he could not possibly carry out, and then behead him for not doing what he was told to do. You might order him, for instance, to build a cathedral for you in one night."

The king was delighted with the advice and sent for the huntsman there and then.

"I want you to build a cathedral for me on that piece of wasteland over there, and if it is not ready by midday tomorrow, your head will be cut off."

The poor huntsman went home much perturbed and told his wife what the king had said to him. "As I can't possibly build a cathedral overnight, we had better run away while there's still time."

"Don't you worry," his wife answered. "Have some supper, say your prayers and go to bed; morning is wiser than evening."

As soon as the huntsman went to sleep, his wife opened her magic book and called out: "My faithful servants! Build me by tomorrow a cathedral on that piece of wasteland over there."

When the king woke up the next morning, he saw that a beautiful cathedral stood in the place he had indicated, and the huntsman was knocking a few last nails in the door. The chamberlain's device had failed and there was no reason to behead the huntsman.

The king was bitterly disappointed, but the chamberlain said, "Never mind; we shall now tell him to make a river flow between your palace and the cathedral and to have ships going down the river—he can never do that." So the king gave this new task to the huntsman and again threatened to behead him if he failed to carry it out.

Once more the huntsman went home looking sad and troubled. He told his wife what the king had said, but she reassured him as before. And, indeed, when he got up in the morning, he saw a river between the cathedral and the palace, and white-sailed ships sailing past. The king saw it, too, and was quite angry with the chamberlain for disappointing him once more.

"Don't be angry, sire," said the wily old man. "This time I have thought of a task which the huntsman will either never fulfill or spend years and years attempting—and meanwhile you can take his wife. Send him there, I know not where, and tell him to get I know not what."

The king followed the chamberlain's advice, and the huntsman went back to his wife more perplexed than ever. This time she, too, was troubled. "It is by far the worst task they have set you," she said. "Go to sleep now and I'll see if I can help you."

When her husband was asleep, she opened her magic book but could find no directions in it. So in the morning she gave him a ball and an embroidered towel. "Roll the ball before you and follow it wherever it goes, and use no towel but this one to wipe your face." Then she kissed him good-by, and he set off on his journey.

In a day or two, the king sent for the huntsman's wife. He came out onto the palace steps to meet her, took her by the hand, and led her to the throne room. "Will you be my queen?" he asked.

"But I have a husband," she said. "I will not desert him, though you be a king and he a poor huntsman."

"Then I shall marry you against your will!" the king cried angrily.

She laughed, changed into a turtledove, and flew out of the window.

Meanwhile her husband walked on and on, following his magic ball. When he came to a river, the ball made itself into a bridge; when he felt tired, the ball became a soft bed. At last he came to a magnificent house and the ball vanished at the gate. He wondered what he had better do and decided to go in.

Three beautiful maidens met him at the door.

"Where do you come from, good man, and what is your errand?"

"Ah, fair maidens, you should give a man time to recover before you question him! I am tired out with my journey."

His hostesses took pity on him, gave him food and drink, and made up a bed for him. When he woke, they brought spring water for him to wash in and an embroidered towel. He thanked them and said he had a towel of his own. When they saw his towel, they asked, "Tell us, good man, where did you get this towel?"

"My wife gave it to me."

"Then you are married to our sister!"

They called their old mother, who at once recognized her daughter's handiwork and was very pleased to meet her son-in-law. He told her his whole story.

The old lady pondered. "I don't know where you are to go and what you are to bring," she said at last, "but I will ask my servants."

She went out to the porch and gave a loud call—and all the birds and beasts and reptiles in the forest gathered around her.

"My son-in-law has to go I know not where and to bring I know not what," she said. "Can anyone tell me what this means?"

No one could tell her, but she saw a lame old frog slowly making its way toward her. "Can you tell me?" she asked.

"Yes, I can," said the frog. "The place he has to go to is very, very far. I could show him the way, but it would take me years and years to get there."

The old lady took a large jar, filled it with fresh milk, and putting the frog into it, told the huntsman to carry it and ask the frog for directions. He said good-by to his mother-in-law and her daugh-

ters and set off. He walked for days and days, the frog pointing the way, and at last came to an enormous bog. The frog turned the huntsman into a straw, took the straw in its mouth, and dived into the bog. At the bottom of it, there stood a splendid house. The frog brought the huntsman to it and told him to hide himself and listen. There was no one in the house; the huntsman hid behind the stove in the front room and waited. In the evening two old men came in and called:

"Afonya, give us something to eat."

No one appeared, but a table was instantly laid for two and furnished with all sorts of dishes and wines. The old men ate and drank their fill, and called out:

"Afonya, clear away."

Everything was removed from the table, and the old men went out again.

The huntsman was very hungry and he wondered if the invisible Afonya would feed him, too. He decided to try his luck and called: "Afonya, give me something to eat."

Immediately a sumptuous meal was set before him. He sat down to it and said:

"Afonya, won't you come and have supper with me? I would be glad of your company."

An invisible voice answered him. "Thank you, good man! I have served the two old men faithfully for thirty years, but they have never asked me to share a meal with them."

The huntsman looked and marveled: he could not see anyone, but the food was disappearing from the plates, the wine glasses were filled and emptied. Presently he asked his invisible companion, "Would you like to join me and be my servant?"

"I would. I am tired of living here, and I see you are a kind man." So they decided to escape from the bog together. Afonya changed into a goose, and the huntsman into a blade of grass. The goose took the grass into its bill and waded out to the dry land. There Afonya became invisible and the huntsman resumed his natural shape. He went to his mother-in-law's house and treated

her and his sisters-in-law to a splendid dinner served by Afonya. Then he took leave of them and started on his journey home.

Presently the road he followed brought him to the seashore; some traders were waiting there for a ship, and they had run out of provisions. The huntsman felt sorry for them and told Afonya to give them dinner. The traders could not believe their eyes when they saw a table laden with excellent food suddenly appear before them, and chairs for them to sit on brought by some invisible hand. They begged the huntsman to sell them his magic servant and offered a tremendous sum of money for him, but the huntsman would not hear of it. Suddenly he heard Afonya whisper to him, "Don't sell me, but exchange me for an empty drum."

The traders readily agreed to give an empty drum in exchange for the invisible servant, and the huntsman walked away with it.

After a time, he grew hungry and said, "I wish I hadn't parted with Afonya! I wonder what he is doing now."

Afonya's voice answered, "I am here, comrade! And here is your dinner."

The huntsman was delighted to have his faithful friend with him again, and after they both had dinner, he asked:

"What is this drum for?"

"Strike it," Afonya answered.

The huntsman struck the drum, and a countless number of soldiers, all fully armed, swarmed around him waiting for orders.

"Strike again," said Afonya.

He struck again and the whole army instantly disappeared.

The huntsman walked on and on. At last he felt so tired that he could scarcely drag his feet. "I wish I could fly!" he said.

"Why didn't you think of that before?" the invisible servant asked, and picking up the huntsman like a straw, carried him through the air straight to his old cottage at the edge of the forest.

The cottage was empty and derelict. The roof had fallen in; cobwebs hung from the rafters. "I cannot stay here," said the huntsman. "Will you build me a house by the sea, Afonya?"

"Yes, of course," the faithful servant answered, and a splendid house with a lovely garden around it close to the sea soon rose up as though of itself.

The huntsman went in and sat down by the window, admiring the flowers. He was thinking how happy he would be if only his wife were with him. All of a sudden, a turtledove flew in, flung itself against the floor, and, behold, his beautiful wife stood before him. They were transported with joy at seeing each other and began talking of all that had happened.

"Ever since you went away I've been flying about in the woods as a turtledove," said his wife.

The following morning, the king came out on his balcony, looked out toward the sea, and saw a fine house close to the beach with a big garden around it.

"How did it come there? And who dared build on my land without my permission?" he asked angrily.

Messengers were sent and they brought the news that it was the huntsman's house, and he and his wife were living there.

The king was enraged and at once sent a detachment of soldiers to seize the huntsman and his wife and destroy their house and garden.

As soon as the huntsman saw the soldiers, he beat his drum, and such a vast army appeared that the king's men ran away at the sight of it. The king understood that he could do nothing against so mighty a host and made peace with the huntsman, promising never to molest him or his wife again. And the huntsman promised, in return, that he would use his army to defend the country should it be attacked by an enemy. After that, he and his wife lived in peace and happiness.

Vassilissa the Fair
and Baba Yagá

There once lived a rich merchant with his wife and daughter. They were very happy together, but one day the wife was taken ill. Feeling that her end was near, she called her little daughter Vassilissa, blessed her, and gave her a doll. "If ever you are in trouble," she said, "ask dolly's advice and she will help you." Thereupon she kissed the child, closed her eyes, and died.

Her husband mourned her deeply and did not want ever to marry again. But presently he heard of a widow with two daughters who were of the same age as his Vassilissa. The widow was reputed to be a good housekeeper, and he thought that with her as stepmother, Vassilissa would be well looked after and have company when he was away from home on business. So he married the widow, but things turned out very differently. The stepmother hated Vassilissa because she was beautiful, kind, and clever, while her own daughters were ugly, stupid, and ill-mannered. She did her best to make her stepdaughter miserable: made her do all the work in the house, gave her the coarsest food, dressed her like a servant, and scolded her from morning till night—nothing Vassilissa did was ever right. Any other girl would have pined away under such treatment, but Vassilissa was protected by her mother's blessing. The doll helped her with the work, and was a great comfort to her. Every evening Vassilissa saved up something from her own scanty supper, put it before the doll, and said:

"Have a bite, dolly, and listen to my unhappy story"—and the doll listened and gave her good advice.

Vassilissa never complained to her father, but he saw for himself what sort of woman his second wife was and did all he could to protect his child from her. Unfortunately he was often away, and on one occasion he had to leave his family for more than a year.

The wicked stepmother decided that this would be a good opportunity to get rid of poor Vassilissa altogether. When her husband had gone, she left the town and moved into a house on the border of a great forest where there lived a terrible ogress, Baba Yagá. The woman took every opportunity of sending Vassilissa to the forest on various errands, in the hope that Baba Yagá would catch her. But the doll took good care of Vassilissa and always brought her safely home. Then the stepmother hatched a new plan, which she confided to her daughters.

In the evening, she gave each of the girls a task to do: one was to make lace, another to knit, and Vassilissa to spin. She left them to it and went to bed. Soon after she had gone, her elder daughter got up to trim the candle, and, as though inadvertently, put out the light. She cried out in pretended alarm:

"What shall we do? There is no light in the house and our tasks aren't half done! One of us will have to go to Baba Yagá to ask for a light!"

"I don't need a light," said her sister. "I am knitting and can see by the light of my needles."

"I don't need it either," said the elder. "I am making lace and the pins give me enough light. Vassilissa must go."

Poor Vassilissa wept and begged them not to send her to Baba Yagá, but they pushed her out of the door, shouting that they would not let her into the house again unless she brought a light from the ogress.

So Vassilissa set out on her errand. It was pitch-dark in the forest, and she walked along picking her way among the trees. A horseman, black from head to foot and mounted on a black horse, rode past her, and the night seemed darker than ever.

Presently a grayish light broke in the sky. A horseman, all in white and mounted on a white horse, rode past her, and it was day. Then the red dawn appeared—after a horseman all in red and mounted on a red horse rode past her—and the sun rose in all its glory.

Vassilissa walked on and on, and toward evening found herself at last before Baba Yagá's house. All around it there was a tall fence crowned with human skulls, and the gates were made of human bones. In the gathering darkness, the eyes of the skulls began to glow, shedding a bright light on the forest clearing. Vassilissa stood spellbound with horror. Suddenly she heard a loud noise: it was Baba Yagá riding in her bowl, pushing it with a pole and sweeping her trail with a broom. The witch rode up to the gates, stopped to sniff the air, and shouted: "Fe-fi-fo-fum! I smell a Russian! Who is here?" Vassilissa came up to her, made a low bow, and said: "It is I, Granny! My stepsisters have sent me to you to beg for a light."

"I know them," said Baba Yagá. "Very well; stay and work for me and if I am satisfied with you, I'll give you a light."

Then she called out: "My strong locks, unlock yourselves! My wide gates, let me in!"

The gates opened, Baba Yagá rode in, whistling loudly; Vassilissa walked in after her, and the gates were shut again.

"Put on the table all that is in the oven. I want my supper," Baba Yagá shouted to Vassilissa.

There was food enough for ten people in the oven, and quantities of mead, beer, and wine in the cellar, but the old witch ate and drank it all, leaving only a little cabbage soup and a chunk of bread for Vassilissa. Then she made ready to go to bed and said: "While I am out tomorrow, you must clean the yard, sweep the floor, cook my dinner, wash the linen, and take from the granary a bushel of wheat and pick out all the black grains from it. And if you don't do it all properly, I'll eat you."

When Baba Yagá began to snore, Vassilissa put all that was left for her supper before the doll and said: "Have a bite, dolly, and listen to my unhappy story! Baba Yagá has set me a heavy task for tomorrow, and threatens to eat me if I don't do it." And she wept bitterly.

But the doll comforted her: "Don't be afraid, dear Vassilissa! Have some supper, say your prayers, and go to bed: morning is wiser than evening."

Vassilissa woke up very early and peeped out of the window: the fire in the skulls' eyes was going out; the white horseman rode past, and it was broad daylight. Baba Yagá went out into the yard, whistled, and her bowl and pole and broom appeared before her. The red horseman went by, and the sun rose. Baba Yagá stepped into the bowl and rode off, pushing it with the pole and sweeping with the broom to cover her tracks. Left alone, Vassilissa stopped to think what work she should do first, but then she saw that everything had already been done, and the doll was picking out the last grains of black from the wheat.

"Ah, my deliverer!" said Vassilissa. "You have saved me from a dreadful peril!"

"All you have to do is to cook the dinner," answered the doll, "and then you can rest in peace."

After sunset, Vassilissa set the table and had everything ready for Baba Yagá. It grew dark, the black horseman rode past the house, and the eyes of the skulls began to glow. There was a loud noise in the forest, grass rustled, branches swayed, trees fell uprooted—it was Baba Yagá arriving. Vassilissa met her in the courtyard.

"Is all the work done?" asked the old witch.

"See for yourself, Granny."

Baba Yagá had a good look around and was annoyed that there was nothing to find fault with. "Very well," she said. "My faithful servants! Grind the wheat!" Three pairs of hands appeared and carried off the grain.

Baba Yagá ate her supper, and before going to sleep, said to Vassilissa: "Do the same tomorrow, and in addition, take a bushel of poppy seeds, sort them out, and throw all the grit away."

In the morning Baba Yagá went off again, and Vassilissa and her doll did all the work. When the old witch came back, she examined everything and called out: "My faithful servants, press the oil out of the poppy seeds." Three pairs of hands appeared, seized the bag with the poppy seeds, and carried it away.

Baba Yagá sat down to her supper while Vassilissa stood by her in silence.

"Why do you stand there like a dumb image and not talk to me?" asked the witch.

"If I may, I would ask you some questions."

"Ask, but be careful: some questions aren't safe to ask. People who know too much grow old before their time."

"I only want to ask about the things I saw on my way to you, Granny. As I walked, a horseman all in black and riding a black horse overtook me. Who is he?"

"That's my dark night," answered Baba Yagá.

"Afterwards another horseman overtook me, all in white, riding a white horse. Who is he?"

"That's my bright day."

"And who is the red horseman riding a red horse?"

"That's my red sun."

Vassilissa thought of the three pairs of hands, but said nothing.

"Why don't you ask more questions?"

"I have asked enough, Granny. You've said yourself that people who know too much grow old before their time."

"It's a good thing you've asked only about things outside the house; I don't like people prying into what's inside. Now I want to ask you a question: how do you manage to do all the work that I set you?"

"My mother's blessing helps me," answered Vassilissa.

"So that's what it is! Then clear out of here at once! I don't want any people with a blessing on them!"

She dragged Vassilissa out of the house, pushed her out of the gates, and snatching a skull from the fence, stuck it on a pole and thrust it into Vassilissa's hands.

"Here is a light for your stepsisters; take it home."

The girl ran as fast as she could from the evil place. She could clearly see her path: the skull shed a bright light and only ceased to glow at the break of day. Vassilissa walked on and on, and in the evening reached her stepmother's house. At the gate she half-thought of throwing the skull away, for she was sure that by now they no longer needed a light, but suddenly she heard a hollow voice coming from the skull: "Take me to your stepmother." Glancing at the house, she saw that there was no light in any of the windows, so she decided to bring in the skull.

For the first time in Vassilissa's life, her stepmother welcomed her home: it appeared that since Vassilissa left, they could not strike a light, and if they borrowed one from neighbors, it went out as soon as they brought it into the house. "I hope your light will keep," said the stepmother. They put the skull in the room where they had been sitting, and it fixed the stepmother and her daughters with its eyes of fire. They could not get away from the glare and by the morning all three were burned to cinders.

Vassilissa buried the skull in the ground, locked up the house, and went to the town. A kind old woman who lived all alone near the town gates took her in, and Vassilissa proved to be a great help and comfort to her.

One day Vassilissa said to the old woman:

"I haven't enough to do, Granny, and I don't like being idle. Please, will you go to the market and buy some of the very best flax for me to spin?"

The old woman bought some flax, and Vassilissa set to work. She could spin beautifully and the thread was even and fine like a hair. When she had spun enough, she wanted to begin weaving, but no loom could be found to take such fine thread. At last she had to ask her doll to provide her with one, and the doll did so in one night. By the spring, Vassilissa had woven all the flax that she had spun, and the linen was so fine that one could thread a needle with it! When the linen had been bleached, Vassilissa said to the old woman: "Sell this linen, Granny, and keep the money for yourself." But the old woman shook her head.

"No, my child," she said. "I would not dream of selling it; such beautiful linen is fit only for the king to wear. I'll take it to him."

She took the linen to the palace, but did not venture to go in. She merely walked up and down in front of it. The king saw her out of the window and called down to ask what she wanted.

"I have brought some rare goods, Your Majesty," answered the old woman, "and I don't want to show them to anyone but you."

The king ordered that she would be admitted, and when he saw the linen, he was astounded. "How much do you want for it?" he asked.

"It's priceless, Your Majesty! I've brought it as a gift to you." The king thanked her and sent her home with rich presents.

The linen was cut to make shirts for the king, but no seamstress would tackle the work: the linen was much too fine, they said. At last the king sent for the old woman and said to her:

"If you know how to spin and weave such linen, you must know how to make shirts of it."

"It was not I, Sire, who spun and wove it, but a young girl who lives with me."

"Well, let her make the shirts."

The old woman went home and told Vassilissa what had happened, and the girl replied: "I knew this task would come into my hands." She shut herself up in her room and set to work. She sewed from morning till night, and soon the dozen shirts were ready. The old woman took them to the king, and meanwhile Vassilissa washed herself, combed her hair, and put on her best dress. Then she sat down at the window and waited.

Presently one of the king's servants came to the door of the house and said:

"The king wants to see the clever worker who made the shirts and to reward her out of his own hands."

Vassilissa went with the king's messenger to the palace and appeared before the king. As soon as he saw her, he loved her with all his heart. He asked her to be his wife, and the wedding was celebrated that very day.

Soon afterwards Vassilissa's father came back and was delighted to find her happily married. Vassilissa asked him to settle with them in the palace, and she also took in the good old woman who had befriended her. They all lived together in love and friendship, and Vassilissa never parted from the doll—her mother's blessing.

The Firebird

Once upon a time there lived a king who had a beautiful garden. It was full of rare and wonderful trees, but the most wonderful of all was an apple tree that bore golden apples. The king valued it greatly and every morning he counted the apples on it to make sure that none has been stolen—though indeed it would not have been easy for any thief to make his way into the garden. There was a high wall of stone all around it, and the gate was always locked at nightfall. And yet one morning the king found that an apple was missing. He thought that he had perhaps made a mistake in counting, but the next day one more apple was gone, and then a third. The king called his three sons together and said to them:

"My dear sons, someone steals a golden apple every night from my precious apple tree; keep watch, and whichever one of you catches the thief shall have half my kingdom while I live and the other half of it after my death."

His eldest son was the first to mount guard by the apple tree, but as night came on, he grew so sleepy that he lay down on the grass and slept till morning. When his father, the king, counted the apples, there was one missing.

The second son fared no better; he, too, was overcome by sleep and did not see anything. By morning another apple was gone.

The third son, Ivan Tsarevitch, was determined to find out who took the apples; he made up his mind not to lie down, and when he felt drowsy, he walked about to keep awake. For hours nothing happened, but at last he saw a bright light in the sky; it rapidly drew nearer and flooded the whole garden. He was so dazzled that at first he could not make out what it was, but presently he saw that the light came from a Firebird that had settled on the apple tree and was pecking one of the apples. He stole up to it and seized the bird by the tail, but it wrenched itself free and flew away, leaving only a feather in Ivan Tsarevitch's hand.

In the morning he went to his father, told him who the thief was, and showed him the Firebird's feather. The king greatly admired the feather which was bright as sunshine. "I wish I could have the Firebird!" he said. "If one of you would capture it for me, I would give him half my kingdom right away, and the other half of it after my death."

All the three sons said they would try and catch the Firebird, and with their father's blessing set forth on the journey. They rode together for a time and then parted company, each going in a different direction.

Ivan Tsarevitch rode for days through fields and woods until he came to an open heath in the middle of which stood a large slab of stone, with an inscription on it: "He who goes straight on shall suffer from hunger and cold; he who goes to the right shall be safe and sound, but his horse will perish; he who goes to the left shall be killed, but his horse will come to no harm." Ivan Tsarevitch read the inscription and went to the right, reflecting that even if his horse was killed, he himself would remain alive. He rode on safely for two days, but on the third day a huge gray wolf met him and said: "Hello, young Ivan Tsarevitch! You have read what is written on the stone, so why do you come this way?" He tore Ivan Tsarevitch's horse to pieces and disappeared.

Ivan Tsarevitch wept and continued his journey on foot. He was

tired out by the end of the day and was just going to sit down and rest when the wolf overtook him. "I am sorry I killed your horse," he said, "so I will let you ride me instead. Tell me where you want to go." Ivan Tsarevitch got onto the wolf's back, told him that he wanted to find the Firebird, and they set off at such a pace that no horseman could have overtaken them. There is no telling how long they journeyed, but at last, in the middle of the night, they came to a low stone wall. The wolf stopped and said to Ivan Tsarevitch: "Climb over this wall; there is a garden on the other side and in the garden hangs a golden cage with the Firebird in it. Take the Firebird, but don't touch the cage or you'll be caught."

Ivan Tsarevitch climbed over the wall and found the cage with the Firebird. He took out the bird and started on his way back, but then he thought, How shall I carry it without a cage? He returned to get the cage, but as soon as he lifted it, there was a tremendous noise. Keepers and gardeners ran out, seized Ivan Tsarevitch, and brought him to their king. The king, whose name was Dalmat, was very angry. "Aren't you ashamed of being a thief, young man? Who are you, and where do you come from?" he asked furiously.

"I am a king's son and my name is Ivan Tsarevitch. Your Firebird came every night to our garden and plucked golden apples from my father's favorite tree, so he bid me find the bird and bring it to him."

"You are a rash young man, Ivan Tsarevitch! This isn't the way to do things. Had you come to me honorably and asked for the Firebird, I would have given it to you—and now I will denounce you to everyone as a thief, and you won't like that. But listen: if you do me a service and procure for me from King Afron the steed with the golden mane, I'll forgive you and make you a present of the Firebird."

Ivan Tsarevitch was greatly perturbed and went to the wolf to tell him what King Dalmat had said.

"Why did you disobey me, Ivan Tsarevitch? I told you not to take the golden cage," said the wolf reproachfully.

"Forgive me; I am much to blame," Ivan Tsarevitch answered.

"Well, never mind. Get onto my back and I'll take you where you want to go."

Ivan Tsarevitch mounted, and the wolf sped away as fast as an arrow. There is no telling how long they journeyed, but at last at dead of night they stopped at King Afron's magnificent stables. The wolf said: "Go into the stables and take the steed with the golden mane; its golden bridle hangs on the wall close by, but don't you touch it! If you do, you'll get into trouble."

Ivan Tsarevitch went into the stables, found the steed with the golden mane, and was on the point of leading it out, when he reflected that it would be very awkward to do so without a bridle. He stretched out his hand for the bridle, but the moment he touched it, there was such a din that all the grooms and stableboys woke up, seized Ivan Tsarevitch, and took him to King Afron. The king was very angry and asked him what his name was and where he had come from. When Ivan Tsarevitch had told him, King Afron said: "You are a foolish young man, Ivan Tsarevitch! That's not the way to do things. Had you come to me openly, I would have given you the steed as a gift, but now I shall have to tell everyone how dishonorably you have behaved. But listen: if you do me a service and bring me Princess Elena the Beautiful from the kingdom at the back of the beyond, I'll forgive you and and will not blacken your name."

Ivan Tsarevitch was greatly distressed. He came to the wolf and told him what had happened. "Ah, you foolish lad! Why did you disobey me and take the golden bridle?"

"I am greatly to blame," said Ivan Tsarevitch.

"Well, never mind," said the wolf. "Get onto my back and I will take you where you want to go." Ivan Tsarevitch did as he was told and the wolf went as fast as the wind. They reached Princess Elena's kingdom and stopped by the golden fence that encircled a beautiful garden. The wolf said: "Now, Ivan Tsarevitch, get down, walk back along the road as far as the big oak tree in the open field, and wait for me there."

Ivan Tsarevitch walked off, and the wolf lay down by the golden fence to wait for Princess Elena the Beautiful. At sunset she came out to take the air with all her ladies and attendants, and as she walked past the place where the wolf was hidden, he jumped over the fence, seized her, and carried her off. He ran as fast as he could to the oak tree in the open field where Ivan Tsarevitch was waiting for him, and said: "Make haste and mount me, Ivan Tsarevitch, and I will take you both to King Afron's kingdom."

Princess Elena's ladies raised the alarm, and horsemen were sent in pursuit, but they could not overtake the wolf and came home empty-handed.

Meanwhile, as Ivan Tsarevitch and Princess Elena the Beautiful journeyed on, they fell in love with each other, and when they came to King Afron's kingdom, Ivan Tsarevitch grew very sad.

"What ails you, Ivan Tsarevitch?" the wolf asked him. "Why are you so sad?"

"How can I help being sad, dear wolf? I have come to love Princess Elena the Beautiful with all my heart, and now I must give her up to King Afron; and if I don't give her to him, he will denounce me as a thief throughout the land."

"I've done a great deal for you, Ivan Tsarevitch," the wolf answered, "and I will do you another service. Listen: I will turn into a beautiful princess and you must bring me to King Afron; he will take me for Princess Elena, and give you the steed with the golden mane. Ride away on it, both of you, as far as you can. Meanwhile, I will go for a walk with all my retinue of ladies, turn into a wolf again, and rejoin you as soon as you think of me."

After saying this, the gray wolf threw himself on the ground and became a beautiful lady. Ivan Tsarevitch led her to King Afron's palace, bidding Princess Elena wait for him outside the city walls.

The king took the beautiful lady to be Princess Elena and was overjoyed at possessing the treasure he had so long coveted. He gave the steed with the golden mane to Ivan Tsarevitch, who rode out of the city, picked up Elena at the appointed place, and went on with her to King Dalmat's kingdom.

The wolf under the guise of Elena the Beautiful spent three days with King Afron and then asked permission to go for a walk in the open fields and enjoy the sight of God's wide world. "There's nothing I would deny you, my beautiful Elena," said the king, and he ordered all the ladies and attendants and maidservants to accompany the princess on her walk. As soon as they came to the open fields, the wolf threw himself on the ground, assumed his natural shape, and ran away.

Ivan Tsarevitch and Elena were talking together as they rode, and had forgotten about the wolf, when suddenly Ivan Tsarevitch thought of him and said, "I wonder where my gray wolf is now." Instantly the wolf stood before him. "Get onto my back, Ivan Tsarevitch, and Princess Elena can ride the golden-maned steed," he said. Ivan Tsarevitch obeyed and they journeyed on to King Dalmat's kingdom.

When they had come within three miles of the capital city Ivan Tsarevitch said to the gray wolf: "You have done me many a service, my good friend, and I would humbly ask you for a last one: could you turn yourself into a golden-maned steed, so that I need not part with this one?"

The wolf threw himself on the ground and turned into a golden-maned steed. Ivan Tsarevitch told the princess to wait for him and took the steed to King Dalmat. The king was delighted and immediately gave him the Firebird in its cage of gold. Ivan Tsarevitch walked with it to the meadow where he had left Elena, and they rode on together to his father's kingdom.

The following day King Dalmat thought he would go for a ride on his splendid new horse, but as soon as he rode into the open country, the horse threw him off, turned into a wolf, and ran away. The wolf soon overtook Ivan Tsarevitch and they continued their journey, the Tsarevitch riding the wolf, and Princess Elena the Beautiful—the golden-maned steed.

When they reached the place where the wolf had killed Ivan Tsarevitch's horse, the wolf said: "I have served you well and faithfully, Ivan Tsarevitch, and now I must leave you." So they said good-by. Ivan Tsarevitch thanked the wolf for all he had done for him, and was very sad at having to part with so good a friend.

There is no telling how long he and the princess journeyed to his father's kingdom, but at last they came within twenty miles of it and stopped to rest on the edge of a wood. They tied the golden-maned steed to a tree, put the cage with the Firebird on the ground, and lay down on the lush green grass. It was a lovely summer's day, and tired with the journey, they dropped fast asleep. And it happened that just then Ivan Tsarevitch's two brothers came riding past. They had been all over the world looking for the Firebird and were returning to their father empty-handed. When they saw Ivan Tsarevitch with all his treasures, they were possessed by bitter envy and killed him in his sleep there and then. Having done this, they awakened Princess Elena the Beautiful and threatened to kill her, too, if she said a word against them to their father. She wept bitterly and called them traitors and murderers, but when they put the points of their swords to her breast, she was frightened and promised not to give them away. So they took her, the golden-maned steed, and the Firebird and rode home.

For three days and nights Ivan Tsarevitch's body lay where he had been slain, and then his friend the gray wolf came upon it. He was grieved to find the Tsarevitch dead and did not know what to do to help him. As he stood there wondering, he saw a raven with two young ones about to alight on the body. The wolf hid himself behind a bush, and as soon as he saw the young ravens pecking at the body, he jumped out and seized one of them. The old raven flew up to him and said: "Don't kill my young child, you gray wolf —it has not done you any harm."

"Listen, Raven," the wolf answered, "I won't hurt your child if you do me a service: fly to the land beyond the sea and bring me some dead water and some living water."

The old raven flew off and in three days' time returned with two small flasks of magic water. The wolf tore the young bird in two and sprinkled it with dead water: the halves grew together again and no trace of the tear was left. He sprinkled it with living water and the young raven revived and flew away. Then the wolf sprinkled Ivan Tsarevitch's body with dead water and the wound in his breast was healed; he sprinkled him with living water and Ivan Tsarevitch opened his eyes, stretched himself, and said, "What an age I've slept!"

"You wouldn't have awakened at all, if it hadn't been for me," the wolf answered. "Your wicked brothers killed you while you were asleep and carried off Princess Elena, the golden-maned steed, and the Firebird. You must hurry home before one of them takes her to wife. Get onto my back and let us go—it will be quicker."

Ivan Tsarevitch mounted the wolf and they arrived at the palace just as the wedding feast was to begin. Elena the Beautiful, pale and sad, was sitting next to the eldest brother as his destined bride. As soon as she saw Ivan Tsarevitch, she jumped up, ran to meet him, and embracing him cried joyfully: "This is my true bridegroom!" She then told the king the whole story of his two elder sons' wickedness. He was so angry that he wanted to cast them both into a dungeon, but Ivan Tsarevitch interceded for them and they were allowed to leave the country and go where they pleased. Ivan Tsarevitch married Princess Elena the Beautiful, and all their life they loved each other so much that they could not bear to be parted for a single day.

Phenist the
Bright-Eyed Falcon

There once lived an old man with his three daughters. The two elder ones loved gaiety and fine clothes, but the third was a quiet, hard-working girl, and very beautiful. When she came out into the village street, the young men could not take their eyes off her.

One day the old man made ready to go to the fair and asked his daughters what they would like him to bring them.

The two elder girls wanted material for new dresses, but the youngest said: "Buy me a red flower, dear Father."

The old man laughed at her. "What do you want with a red flower, my little silly? There's no use in it. I'd better bring you some piece of finery." But he could not persuade her—all she wanted was a red flower.

The father said good-by, got into his cart, and drove to the town. He bought the presents which his elder daughters had asked for at the fair, but could not find a red flower anywhere, though he searched for it all over the town. He was sorry to disappoint his favorite daughter, but she said: "Never mind—maybe you'll have better luck another time."

The elder sisters laughed at the youngest as they were cutting out and sewing their new dresses, but she never answered their taunts.

Presently their father again made ready to go to the fair and again asked them what presents they would like. The two elder girls asked for a kerchief each, and the third said: "Buy me a red flower, dear Father."

He took leave of his family and drove to the town. He bought two fine kerchiefs, but a red flower was not to be seen anywhere. And again his youngest daughter said: "Never mind—perhaps you will find it some other day."

The old man had to go to the fair a third time. "What would you like me to buy for you, my daughters?" he asked. The two elder girls wanted earrings, and the youngest once more begged him: "Buy me a red flower, dear Father."

He bade them good-by, got into his cart, and drove to the town. He bought golden earrings and began looking for a red flower. He went all over the fair, but no one had such a thing to sell. Greatly vexed, he started on his way home, but no sooner had he driven out of the city gates than he saw an old man carrying a red flower.

"Sell me your flower, good man," he said.

"It is not for sale, but if your youngest daughter agrees to marry my son, Phenist* the Bright-Eyed Falcon, I will make you a present of it."

The father hesitated: not to take the flower meant disappointing his daughter and to take it meant marrying her to goodness knows who! But on reflection he decided to take the flower. If we don't like the suitor, we can refuse him after all, he thought.

When he came home, he gave the earrings to the elder sisters, and the red flower to the youngest, and as he did so he said to her: "I don't like your flower at all, my dear daughter." Then he whispered in her ear: "It was not for sale, you know; it was given me by

---

* Phenist is probably a corruption of Phoenix—in Egyptian mythology a bird of great beauty.

an unknown old man on condition that you marry his son, Phenist the Bright-Eyed Falcon."

"Don't worry, Father! He is good and kind. He flies about in the sky as a falcon and then he flings himself against the ground and becomes a fine young man."

"Do you know him, then?"

"Yes, Father. He was in church last Sunday and kept looking at me, and I spoke to him afterwards. He loves me, you know."

The old man shook his head, looked at his daughter thoughtfully, and said: "Go up to your room, dear child; it's bedtime. Morning is wiser than evening—we will talk tomorrow."

His daughter locked herself in her room, put the red flower in water, opened the window, and gazed into the blue distance.

All of a sudden a bright-colored falcon flew in, flung itself against the floor, and became a handsome young man. The maiden was frightened at first, but as soon as he spoke to her, she felt wonderfully happy and lighthearted. They talked together till dawn; as soon as it began to grow light, Phenist the Bright-Eyed Falcon kissed her and said: "Every night, as soon as you put the red flower in the window, I will come to you, sweetheart. And here is a feather from my wing for you: if you want anything, come out onto the porch and wave it to the right—and instantly all that you wish will be brought to you."

He kissed her again, turned into a falcon, and flew away beyond the dark forest. The maiden followed him with her eyes, closed the window, and went to bed.

After that, her betrothed flew in to her every night as soon as she put the red flower in the window. Sunday came. The church bells began ringing. The elder sisters made ready to go to Mass; they put on their new dresses and kerchiefs and golden earrings and mocked their youngest sister. "And what are you going to wear, you clever one? You have no new clothes! You'd better stay at home with your red flower."

"Don't trouble about me, dear sisters! I can say my prayers at home."

The sisters went off in all their finery, and she sat down by the window and watched good people going to church. When all had gone by, she came out onto the front steps, waved the falcon's feather to the right, and suddenly there appeared before her a coach made of crystal driven by splendid horses, servants in golden livery, and beautiful apparel for herself.

She dressed, got into the coach, and drove to church. The people gazed at her and marveled at her beauty. "It must be some princess from over the sea," they said.

She left just before the end of the service and drove away; no one saw her go. When she got home, she waved the feather to the left, and instantly the coach and the servants disappeared and she was wearing her old dress once more. She went and sat at the window as though nothing had happened and watched the people returning from church. Her sisters came home in great excitement, and as soon as they saw her, they both said at once: "Do you know, there was a most beautiful lady in church today! She must be some foreign princess. Her dress was simply magnificent!"

Another Sunday came, and a third, and she played the same game. But the last time, when she came home from church, she forgot to take a diamond pin out of her hair. Her elder sisters began telling her about the beautiful princess, and all of a sudden they noticed that a diamond was sparkling in their youngest sister's braids. "Whatever have you got in your hair?" they cried. "Why, the princess wore exactly the same kind of pin! How did you come by it?"

She cried out and ran to her room. Her sisters pestered her with questions, whispered together, and made guesses, but she never said a word and only laughed to herself. Then they began spying on her and listening at her door. One night they overheard her talking with Phenist the Bright-Eyed Falcon, and at dawn saw him fly out of her window and disappear behind the dark forest.

The elder sisters were spiteful girls: they contrived to conceal sharp knives on the youngest one's windowsill so that Phenist the

Bright-Eyed Falcon should cut his wings. She did not notice anything, placed the red flower in the window as usual, and went to sleep.

In the night Phenist the Bright-Eyed Falcon flew up to the window, but he could not get in: the sharp knives barred his way and he cut his wings against them. "Good-by, fair maiden," he said at last. "You'll have to seek me over the hills and far away, at the uttermost ends of the earth. You will wear out three pairs of iron boots, break down three iron staffs, and gnaw three loaves made of stone before you find me, your own true love."

The maiden heard these cruel words through her sleep, but wake up she could not. When morning came she opened her eyes and saw sharp knives stuck crisscross in the window with their blades upward, and red blood was dripping from them onto the flower.

She wept long and bitterly and spent many a sleepless night at her open window, but the falcon never came again. She waved his feather, but nothing happened—his servants no longer waited on her.

At last she went to her father and, weeping, asked for his blessing to go in search of her bridegroom. She had three pairs of iron boots made, three iron staffs, and three loaves of stone, and set off in the direction from which Phenist the Bright-Eyed Falcon used to come to her.

For days and days she trudged through the forest, picking her way among fallen trees and tree stumps. Her iron boots were wearing out, her staff was breaking, her stone loaf was falling to pieces, and the forest grew darker and more dense as she walked on.

Then she saw before her a tiny hut on hen's feet that kept turning around and around.

The maiden said: "Little hut, little hut! Turn your back to the forest and your front to me." The hut turned and she walked in.

A Baba Yagá lay on the floor stretched right across the room, her nose reaching almost to the ceiling.

"Fe-fi-fo-fum!" she said. "In the old days there was no sight or smell of a Russian in these parts, and now Russians stalk about the world and come of their own accord! Where are you going, fair maid? Are you fleeing from duty or pursuing a goal?"

"I was betrothed to Phenist the Bright-Eyed Falcon, Granny, but my sisters did him a wrong. I want to find him."

"You have far to go, poor child! He lives at the back of the beyond where the four winds meet, and he thinks of marrying a foreign princess who has bewitched him."

Baba Yagá gave the maiden meat and drink, and put her up for the night. She roused her at daybreak and said:

"Go, with God's blessing, to my elder sister—she will help you. And here is my present for you: a silver distaff and a golden spindle. When you come to Phenist's kingdom by the blue sea, his betrothed will want to buy these things from you. Don't take anything she offers, but by way of payment ask to see Phenist the Bright-Eyed Falcon."

Then Baba Yagá took a ball of thread, threw it on the path, and said: "Follow it; it will show you the way."

The maiden thanked the old woman and went on her way. The forest closed around her and seemed to grow darker and more dense as she walked on. She walked for days and days and her second pair of iron boots wore out, and her second iron staff broke, and the second loaf of stone crumbled away. At last the ball rolled up to a hut on hen's feet that was turning around and around.

"Little hut, little hut!" the maiden said, "turn your back to the forest and your front to me. I make the request, for I come as a guest."

The hut obeyed, turned frontwards, and the maiden went in. A second Baba Yagá, more ancient and bony than the first, was in the hut. "Fe-fi-fo-fum!" she said. "In the old days there was no sight or smell of a Russian in these parts, and now Russians come here of their own accord! Where are you going, fair maid?"

"I was betrothed to Phenist the Bright-Eyed Falcon, Granny. My sisters did him an injury, and now I am in search of him."

"Ah, my poor child, your Phenist will soon marry another; they are celebrating their betrothal today," said Baba Yagá. Then she gave the maiden supper, made up a bed for her, and the following morning roused her before sunrise and gave her a fine present—a silver saucer and a golden egg.

"Take this," she said, "and go to my elder sister; she'll give you good advice. And when you come to Phenist's kingdom by the blue sea, and his betrothed walks past you, roll the golden egg in the silver saucer. She will want to buy it from you, but don't take anything from her—only ask her to let you see Phenist the Bright-Eyed Falcon."

The maiden thanked the old woman, sighed, and throwing the ball of thread on the ground, followed its lead.

Again she went through the dark forest that seemed to grow denser and denser, the treetops reaching to the sky. She walked on for days and days and at last her third pair of boots wore out, the third staff broke down, the third loaf of stone crumbled away, and she came to a hut on hen's feet that was turning around and around. The maiden said:

"Little hut, little hut! Turn your back to the forest and your front to me! I make the request, for I come as a guest."

The hut obeyed and she walked in. In the hut was a Baba Yagá, the most ancient of the three. She welcomed the maiden and asked her what her errand was.

"I am looking for my betrothed, Phenist the Bright-Eyed Falcon, Granny. My sisters injured him and he flew away from me to a far-off land at the back of the beyond where the four winds meet."

"You poor, poor child! Your Phenist is marrying a foreign princess. The wedding day has already been fixed," said Baba Yagá. She gave the maiden food and drink and made up a bed for her; the following morning she woke her at daybreak and gave her a present—a golden needle and an embroidery frame.

"Now go, fair maid, and God speed you! Lose no time. When you come to Phenist's kingdom, take out the embroidery frame; you only have to hold it, and the needle will do the embroidering of itself. The princess will want to buy it from you, but don't take anything for it—only ask to see Phenist the Bright-Eyed Falcon."

The maiden thanked the old woman, wept bitterly, and throwing down the ball, followed its lead.

The forest grew less dense and presently she saw before her the blue sea sparkling in the sun. On the shore there lay a beautiful city, the golden cupolas of its white turrets shining like fire in the morning light.

This must be Phenist's kingdom, thought the maiden. She sat down on the sand, took out her silver distaff and golden spindle, and began spinning golden thread.

At that moment the foreign princess with her ladies and attendants appeared on the beach. As soon as she saw what the maiden was doing, she wanted to buy her spindle and distaff.

"Let me have a look at Phenist the Bright-Eyed Falcon, Princess, and you can have them as a gift," said the maiden.

"Phenist is alseep just now, and he said he did not want to be disturbed; but so be it! I'll let you in to him if you give me your silver distaff and golden spindle."

The princess seized the things, ran to the palace, and stuck a magic pin in Phenist the Falcon's coat to prevent him waking. Then she ordered her attendants to take the maiden to his room and went for her morning walk.

The maiden wept long and bitterly, trying to rouse Phenist the Bright-Eyed Falcon. "Awake, arise, my beloved! It is I, your true love, who has come to you. I've broken down three iron staffs, worn out three pairs of iron boots, gnawed three loaves of stone while I've been seeking you."

But he slept and could not wake.

Having walked her fill, the princess came back, drove the maiden away, and took the magic pin out of Phenist the Falcon's coat.

He woke up and said:

"I've overslept! Someone has been here, weeping and lamenting over me, but I could not open my eyes, and my heart felt so heavy."

"It must have been a dream," the princess said. "No one came in here."

The following morning, the maiden again sat on the beach, rolling a golden egg in a silver saucer.

The princess came out for a walk, saw her, and at once wanted to buy the things. The maiden said, "You can have them as a gift if only you let me see Phenist the Bright-Eyed Falcon." The princess agreed, and again stuck the magic pin in Phenist's coat.

Again the maiden wept bitterly, trying to awaken him. "Rise up, my beloved! It is I, your own true love, who has come to you! Long have I sought you and at last I have found you, but now I call you, and you give me no answer."

Phenist the Bright-Eyed Falcon slept on and could not wake. The princess came back, drove the maiden away, and took the magic pin out of Phenist's coat.

"I've slept too long! Someone has been here, weeping and lamenting over me, but I could not open my eyes and my heart felt so heavy."

"Oh, you dreamed it. There has been no one in the room," said the princess.

On the third morning, the maiden sat on the seashore, looking pale and sad. She held the golden embroidery frame in her hands and the needle embroidered by itself.

The moment the princess saw this she wanted to buy the frame at any price. "You can have it as a gift if only you let me see Phenist the Bright-Eyed Falcon," the maiden said. The princess agreed, ran to the palace, and said to Phenist: "Let me comb your hair." As she was combing it, she concealed the magic pin in his hair and he dropped asleep at once; then she sent her servants for the maiden.

The maiden came and for the last time tried to wake her bridegroom. She spoke to him, and fondled him, but it was of no avail. Weeping bitterly, she kissed him and stroked his hair, and as she did so, she inadvertently caused the magic pin to fall out. Phenist the Bright-Eyed Falcon woke up, and great was his joy when he recognized his true love.

She told him all that had happened: how her spiteful sisters had envied her, how she had sought him, and how she bargained with the foreign princess.

Thereupon he summoned his nobles and warriors and men of every estate to council and asked them:

"Tell me, which wife should I marry: the one who sold me, or the one who ransomed me?"

All the nobles and warriors and men of every estate answered in one voice: "The one who ransomed you."

So Phenist the Bright-Eyed Falcon married his true love, and they lived happily ever after.